Praise for *Focused F*

"**Focused Forward** *gets it! If you or someone you care about has the adult version of ADHD, read this book. Written by a man who's worked in the trenches his whole career, this book is full of practical tips as well as a deep understanding for what this widely misunderstood condition is truly like. A hugely valuable contribution to the treatment of adult ADHD.*"

—**Edward M. Hallowell, M.D.**
New York Times bestselling author of *Driven to Distraction*

"*James Ochoa's new book,* **Focused Forward: Navigating the Storms of Adult ADHD** *is very moving, easy to read, and reflects the obvious depth of the author's clinical experience. This book could only have been written by someone who has spent many years successfully guiding adults to navigate the complex storms of adult ADHD. This book is a rare combination of warmth, wisdom, and innovative tools that can sooth the ADHD soul!*

I have already started recommending this book to my clients! Mr. Ochoa's ground-breaking concept of the Emotional Distress Syndrome profoundly affects countless adults with adult ADHD and now gives clinicians and adults a previously missing but critical understanding that can lead to healing the wounds of the accumulated assaults of growing up with ADHD."

—**Sari Solden, MS, LMFT**
Psychotherapist and bestselling author of *Women with Attention Deficit Disorder* and *Journeys Through ADDulthood*

"Finally, a book that gets to the heart of the matter! James Ochoa breaks the silence and brings a voice to possibly the most devastating and misunderstood aspect of ADHD—the emotional distress. He offers practical tools and coping strategies to help people with ADHD close the gap between surviving and thriving. This book is a must for people with ADHD, their loved ones and their helping professionals!"

—Nancy A. Ratey, Ed.M., MCC
Best-Selling Author of *The Disorganized Mind*

"If you've struggled to make sense of your adult ADHD brain, **Focused Forward: Navigating the Storms of Adult ADHD** *is the owner's manual you've been waiting for."*

—Christie Sprowls, Psy.D

"James Ochoa has a unique perspective on the emotional stress of ADHD— he has the disorder himself and he's spent his career working with ADHD adults. I believe there's a tremendous need for this book, **Focused Forward: Navigating the Storms of Adult ADHD.** *As a cognitive behavioral therapist, I'm no stranger to patients who can describe the emotional distress of ADHD in vivid personal detail, without knowing what it's called, let alone how to address it. Indeed, as far as I know, James Ochoa is the first clinician not just to identify this all-too-common syndrome, but to brainstorm unique fixes. The techniques and stories in this book will serve as a valuable adjunct to cognitive therapy—making it invaluable to patient and therapist alike. If you strive for emotional health, pick up this book!"*

—Lawrence P. Bachus, Ph.D.

"The tools in this book are what I have been looking for ever since I was diagnosed with ADHD. I have used most of the techniques for dealing with the external world. They have all helped, but only to a point. I was missing the techniques for dealing with my internal world but could not find them, until now. I dove into the middle of the book, as James suggested for someone like me, and found techniques that I was able to immediately put to use. I look forward to integrating these ideas into my life and passing them on to my clients. It is my personal opinion that this book could also be valuable to those that are not ADHD but are being stressed by the hectic modern world we live in. That could be just about anyone!"

—**Tom Viets**
ADHD Life Coach

"As a classroom teacher, reading specialist and dyslexia therapist for the past 30+ years, I have taught and experienced numerous students with ADHD. **Focused Forward: Navigating the Storms of Adult ADHD** *was quite enlightening and informative for me because it helped me understand this disorder at a deeper level. As I read the book, many of my past and present students came to mind and what they go through as a person with this disorder. It will be a book of reference for me, and I have even implemented a few of the strategies with some of my students, and the response was very positive. I feel a much stronger compassion for these students now."*

—**Mary Cook**
Academic Language Therapist at
Rawson Saunders School in Austin

"**Focused Forward: Navigating the Storms of Adult ADHD,** *by James Ochoa, is a small but powerful book that will change lives for those with ADHD and their significant others who read it. The style of writing is extremely user-friendly with each section flowing seamlessly into the next. It is full of valuable information about the diagnosis of ADHD, particularly for adults, along with practical and relevant strategies that can be of immediate help to those persons struggling with the emotional impact of ADHD in their lives. The uniqueness of this book is the very personal and authentic stories that the author, himself a therapist, shares of his own struggles in living his life with ADHD, stories that will resonate with and touch the hearts of all who read it. Focused Forward is a much-needed and important addition to the resources available on ADHD."*

—Rona Pogrund, Ph.D.
Professor
Texas Tech University
College of Education-Special Education Program

"Insightful and plain spoken, this book goes to the heart of what can be the crippling self-doubt and self-sabotage of adult ADHD. The analogy in the title to a 'storm' is a very powerful image for the ADHD individual who has often struggled for years. The diagnosis of Emotional Distress Syndrome captures that overwhelming sense of private hopelessness with a public face that is maintained to attempt functioning with a crippling emotional distress."

—Kern Vanderburg
Business Development Professional

FOCUSED forward

NAVIGATING
the storms of
Adult ADHD

JAMES M. OCHOA, LPC

Navigating the Storms of Adult ADHD
By James M. Ochoa

Empowering Minds Press

Published by Empowering Minds Press, Austin, Texas

Editor: Robin Chotzinoff, chotzinoff@gmail.com
Copyeditor: Jane Le, janele@comcast.com
Proofreader: Lisa Canfield, www.copycoachlisa.com
Index: Elena Gwynn, www.QuillAndInkIndexing.com
Art direction: Kim Iberg, Art Ranch, kimdiberg@gmail.com
Cover and interior design: Davis Creative, www.DavisCreative.com
Cover illustration: Kim Iberg, ArtRanch, kimdiberg@gmail.com
Cover copy: Lisa Canfield, www.copycoachlisa.com
Author's photo's: Amy Melsa, www.amymelsaphotography.com

Library of Congress Control Number: 2015920432
ISBN: 978-0-9969839-0-7

ATTENTION CORPORATIONS, UNIVERSITIES, COLLEGES AND PROFESSIONAL ORGANIZATIONS: Quantity discounts are available on bulk purchases of this book for educational, gift purposes, or as premiums for increasing magazine subscriptions or renewals. Special books or book excerpts can also be created to fit specific needs. For information, please contact Empowering Minds Press, 2111 Dickson Street, Suite 14, Austin, Texas 78704.

In memory of Dr. Byron Kocen,
Keith Miller,
and
Carol York
all wise teachers and steadfast friends.

TABLE OF CONTENTS

FOREWORD

A llow me to introduce you to James Ochoa, my esteemed colleague and very good friend. James and I met more than twenty years ago, and we're still working, laughing and celebrating life together. One of our favorite things to do is to meet at Ladybird Lake to walk, talk and sort things out—and to welcome the sun coming up on a new day. It was during those early morning walks that I first heard James describe the concepts you're about to encounter in *Focused Forward: Navigating the Storms of Adult ADHD.*

Much has been written for adults with ADHD, but very little about the emotional stress that goes hand in hand with the condition. Emotional stress is James Ochoa's bailiwick—it's what he covers so thoroughly in this book, what he addresses in his busy, successful practice, and what he confronts honestly in himself. These days, the ADHD diagnosis has become more familiar, carrying less of a stigma. But the emotional stress concept is still profoundly new, not just to those diagnosed with ADHD, but to therapists and clinicians as well. Identifying the emotional stress of ADHD, and developing so many ways to overcome it, has made James into what I always knew he would be: a thought leader in his field.

If you've struggled to make sense of your adult ADHD brain, *Focused Forward: Navigating the Storms of Adult ADHD* is the owner's manual you've been waiting for. You'll learn unusual (even entertaining) techniques that will improve your life and the lives of the people around you. James has woven together a fabric of ways to thrive, putting them to the test countless times in his own life and in the lives of his clients at The Life Empowerment Center. I honestly think anyone could use the material in this book to change his or her life for the better. If you're a therapist, you should arm yourself with sticky notes and a highlighter, because James' book is full of tools you can use.

Perhaps you can tell I'm James Ochoa's biggest champion. I am. As any of his clients would tell you, he is an easy man to know and trust. More importantly, his work is truly groundbreaking. James has helped a lot of people, and with the publication of this book, he's about to help many, many more.

—Christie Sprowls, Psy.D

ACKNOWLEDGEMENTS

It's beyond important that I thank the many people who helped with the development of my ideas, up to and including the writing of this book, over the many years it took me to make it real. So, my heartfelt thanks:

To all the many colleagues and friends whose support never wavered.

To the many clients who had the courage to face the distress of their ADHD diagnosis, and who trusted me enough to help them find a way to reconnect to themselves.

To Kim Lauritzen, for managing The Life Empowerment Center and organizing me—not easy jobs, and yet there you still are, after all these years!

To Robin Chotzinoff, my writing coach, whose gift for translating ideas, inspirations and life experiences made the writing of this book an adventure I could never have imagined.

To Kim Iberg, master illustrator and designer of my book and its cover—at the eleventh hour, no less.

To my late parents, Al and Juanita, whose love, tenacity and courage enabled them to stay married for 58 years. My mom was my greatest advocate through all my learning challenges. My dad was the best story-teller I—or anyone who ever met him—ever knew. He taught his children that true happiness depends on just three things: deep-loving relation-ships, telling stories, and having fun.

To my brothers Al, David, John, Paul, and Michael, for being all—and more—than a family should be. And to my dear and only sister, Mary, whose work as a reading specialist has taught her so much about ADHD, and who has championed my work. And in memory of my brother Ron, who died in 2005, but not before teaching us about unconditional love.

To my sons, Gabe and Jules, who continue to be my greatest teachers, many times over. May you continue to follow your passions and dreams.

And finally to Edie Vitemb-Ochoa, the love of my life, who has supported my visions throughout our marriage, even when I disrupted our lives in funny and not-so-funny ways. Edie, you are my friend, my comrade-in-arms, and one of the most gifted and dedicated teachers ever to make a mark on countless Austin children. I may fancy myself a navigator, but you are my compass. I truly don't know where I'd be without you.

INTRODUCTION

Most people who walk into my office have had damn good therapy over the years. A lot of them have been very successful. Some have been diagnosed with ADHD, some are second-guessing a second, third or fourth diagnosis. They wonder if they really have it—or what "it" really means. However long it takes, the diagnosis comes with a sense of recognition and, at first, a deep feeling of relief.

But people don't come to me for counseling to discuss how contented they are. They're not. Something is wrong. Some *things* are wrong! A lot of things aren't right—everything from catastrophic lives to a vague sense of disconnection that persists, year after year.

Or maybe, even after being diagnosed with ADHD and getting on the right meds and working with a coach and learning where to keep their car keys, they somehow still don't understand who they are.

Or maybe, even though they know ADHD hasn't affected their IQs, or the knowledge they gained of the world as a kid—their mastery of how to climb a tree or ride a bike—they still don't seem to reach their potential, even when they look reasonably successful to the outside world. Somehow, the ADHD disrupts it. There's a grand canyon between their potential and their performance.

Or maybe they lose their train of thought multiple times each day. They get physically fidgety. And it's more than ADHD; it's a creeping sense of overwhelm, a darkness rolling out of the dawn. They've screwed up, and not for the first or last time. The other shoe is hanging there, waiting to drop.

Or maybe they were diagnosed with ADHD but refused to believe it was true. Maybe they went into denial for one, two or twenty years, and the shoe kept dropping again and again, and their denial could no longer hold back the disruption.

Maybe this person is you, reading this book. Or maybe someone who loves you is reading this book, trying to understand you. I know this person is me, writing this book, telling you there's more to a diagnosis of ADHD than understanding, managing and scheduling. Because we've all done our best to manage all that—right? There's also the constant, corrosive stress of a lifetime of wondering what the hell is wrong with you, what is still wrong with you, the scrambling to undo your latest damage, whether real or imagined.

Twenty-five years as a professional specializing in ADHD have shown me that I'm not alone in living with this pervasive sense of dread and stress. I call it the Emotional Distress Syndrome (EDS) of ADHD, and I've come to believe it's very much like post-traumatic stress disorder, except that it can't be traced to specific instances of danger or trauma. But living with ADHD produces its own chronic, all-encompassing emotional stress until you learn to deal with it.

Maybe this sounds familiar to you. It usually does to my clients. Here's a striking comment from a man who'd read one of my articles but hadn't yet seen me in person for therapy:

"Failures in life cause EDS. I feel I know what the outcome is going to be and I don't want to take a chance. I venture nothing and I gain nothing (as they say). Actions as simple as balancing a checkbook may expose the fact that I'm insolvent."

Here's another thought, from another new client, also before our first meeting:

"I would very much like to repair the seeming mental short-circuit that has led to being perennially late my whole life; I want to reverse the increase of absentmindedness; improve concentration at work; reduce my anxiety. I'm afraid, given how damaged my family of origin is, of discovering that I am broken and/or 'crazy' in some fashion."

Of course, this guy didn't turn out to be broken or crazy, just depleted from years of emotional distress.

Emotional distress—it sounds so commonplace, so non-particular to any psychological condition. But it's as specific as it is unsettling. If you're an adult with ADHD, you might recognize parts of yourself.

You know you're smart, you know you know what to do, but you're inconsistent. Consistently inconsistent! Whatever you do works for a while, but then it's less interesting; it falls off your schedule or routine. Or there's something about your otherwise not-too-shabby brain that doesn't remember that schedule—or really, any schedule. Your system was working yesterday, but now everyone's looking at you and you're at a loss for words and you say *I don't know, the battery ran out in my timer, the alarm didn't go off again this morning, I didn't do this on purpose*. But if it wasn't your fault, why are the accusatory voices coming from your own head so very nasty?

You're in the sea again, in the storm, wondering how you got there. The people around you can't really see what you're experiencing. And if they can't see it, why should they believe it? Or if they know you—if, say, they live with you—they might just be tired of all these storms. After a while, you find it easier to lose consideration for those other people, the people who don't seem to understand.

It's hard to predict what might set off a storm—an innocuous or curious question that zeroes in on your sense of failure, your missed expectations, your unresolved answers, that kick the chair out from under you. Whoever's asking doesn't even know how they're affecting you. And once again, you're spiraling in the Emotional Distress Syndrome.

If you don't know how to reset yourself, who knows where it ends? I've seen tiny, supposedly inconsequential triggers send someone into a two-year spiral, during which they lose themselves. That gap, that chasm, is the very essence of the Emotional Distress Syndrome of ADHD. I don't care how many behavioral strategies or medications you try, it does nothing at the end of the day if you don't treat the emotional stress.

You may not be optimistic about the possibility of getting some balance and joy back in your life, but I am, and I've got many years of clinical experience to back me up. I look forward to introducing you to the many different techniques that have helped me and so many of my clients with ADHD, and to sharing some of their experiences.

If you don't know what I'm talking about, that's fine. You may never have experienced the feeling of being sure of yourself, of having clarity about your decisions. You may not know what it's like to be able to handle a setback, big or small. To calm and reset yourself after something throws you off track. But these are skills you can learn, and the learning begins with your relationship with yourself.

So stay with me. We're going to walk across the fields of neuroscience, psychology, spirituality and imagination. Although I know a lot about ADHD, having a reasonably serious case of it myself, I'm still learning a lot about reaching my potential. It is my hope that you will, too.

Before we get into the nitty-gritty, though, a few words about navigation and the North Star.

At some point during the *long* process of writing this book, I had to come to terms with the fact that although I'd identified a very real issue—the Emotional Distress Syndrome of ADHD—I wasn't going to be able to offer my clients a simple solution, a miracle cure or an effortless intervention. ADHD, and the emotions that go along with it, can't be eradicated, erased or blasted into a million pieces. But they *can* be managed, in a very personalized way. It's a lifelong process. It takes commitment.

Not very sexy, right?

And yet I've come to feel so hopeful about this process. I've seen things go so right for so many of my clients and friends that I've come to think that dealing with ADHD and its emotional fallout is more like *navigating* than *managing*. Managers spend a lot of time sitting at a desk, looking at a screen. Navigators travel the world. That alone should be enough to keep us interested!

But let's take it a step further. Imagine charting the course of your unique life as an epic sea voyage. You'd be prepared to make constant adjustments at the helm depending on the winds and weather—some of which you could predict, some of which you couldn't. Or imagine this life journey as a trek through an uninhabited mountain wilderness. You'd need to orient yourself every step of the way, figure out where you were going, and adjust for whatever nature threw at you. You'd want to have a very clear idea of who you were, and where, exactly, you'd like to end up.

You'd get some insight from fellow explorers, but in the end, you'd have to blaze your own trail.

Interestingly, no matter what kind of adventure you consider yourself to be undertaking, whether by land or by sea—or boardroom, laptop or sofa—you share one simple navigational tool with the rest of humanity. You can teach yourself to find the North Star: Polaris, the star that lines up with the axis of the earth, the star that holds steady while the other stars move around it. From wherever you happen to be, the North Star will always help you get your bearings. Though some poets have claimed otherwise, Polaris isn't the brightest light in the galaxy, just a star of average brilliance. But, really, how brilliant is that?

I like knowing it's out there. I thought you might, too. You can find your own North Star inside of you. Better yet, you can look ahead, chart a course and move toward a future of your own design. Yes, you can be *focused forward*.

Now that we're oriented, let's begin.

> *"It's easy to keep track of art by what it's not. It's not following a manual, looking at a map. It tends to be people who work with a compass instead, who have an understanding of true north and are willing to solve a problem in an interesting way."*
> —Seth Godin

HOW TO READ THIS BOOK

We who have ADHD do not gravitate to linear thinking. Or reading, I've noticed. Therefore, I've designed this book to be read by someone with a wandering mind. You can, of course, start at the beginning and read straight through to the end. And if you don't have ADHD and are trying to understand the condition, this is the way to go. But if you'd rather plan your own route, I'll give you a quick overview:

Part One: We, With Our ADHD is divided into two parts. The first, "Me and My ADHD," contains my story—from early childhood to the present, with an emphasis on the role ADHD has played in my life. If you feel some urgency about your own ADHD, you can skip this part and come back to get to know me later.

"You and Your ADHD" covers the basic drill for an ADHD adult, from symptoms to diagnosis to medications to coaching. It's a summary of the interventions that are probably available to you at this time. It will take most of us with ADHD right up to the point of realizing that there is such a thing as emotional distress, and that, in fact, no one much is talking about it! Then, of course, I'll start talking about it.

Part Two: Weathering the Storm goes into the nitty-gritty of the Emotional Distress Syndrome, from what precipitates it to how it can be managed and alleviated. It introduces the therapeutic tools I've used for decades in my practice. If you picked up this book for immediate help with the emotional distress of ADHD, this is where you should start.

Part Three: Advanced Life Empowerment is a compendium of lessons I've learned in my years as a therapist and clinician. There are sections on dealing with children, marriage, and talking to the loved ones in your life who don't have ADHD. Of particular interest, I think, is

"Mayday! Mayday! Staying the Course During a Storm" an emergency-preparedness chapter designed to help you weather the worst storm your brain chemistry can manufacture.

Throughout this book, you may see special sections titled "Try This at Home." They should be self-explanatory.

Finally, you'll find numerous quotes offered anonymously by a large sample of my clients at The Life Empowerment Center. These people were so kind—not just to respond to my questionnaires and write very detailed responses, but to have given me honest feedback all these years whenever I came up with something new to try. They have been my pioneer navigators, and I am grateful to them all.

PART ONE

WE, WITH OUR ADHD

ME AND MY ADHD

One of the first things I do every morning when I walk into my office at The Life Empowerment Center, is turn on the little light next to the tabletop babbling brook fountain. The babbling brook stays on 24/7, at my request. The sound of moving water has always calmed my brain chatter better than any other intervention, and it took me a long time to find a miniature fountain that seemed exactly right. Somehow, I never get tired of being welcomed into my workplace by one of my favorite sounds. And when I look around this office, once again, every day, I feel grateful to be here.

In some ways, it's a million miles from the place I grew up. In reality, it's only about a three-hour drive.

I'm originally from Houston. I come from a family of eight kids, most just about one year apart, seven of us boys. I was number seven, near the bottom of the heap. Between this crowded, dynamic family and hours of playing sports on the street, I learned the theory of organized chaos first-hand. It always made perfect sense to me that I became a counselor, and that my major theoretical orientation is Family Systems Theory.

I was a difficult child at times. I threw serious tantrums. I questioned or challenged many directions I received—unless I ignored them alto-gether and took off impulsively in a different direction. I likely could have been diagnosed with Oppositional Defiant Disorder. Anyway, that's what was wrong.

But then I ended up in the hospital, for eight weeks—and that experience, believe it or not, is what sent my life in a different, more optimistic direction. I was only four years old when it happened. I was playing on my parents' parked car and I fell off of it, hitting my head on the concrete. The doctors told my mother that blood was leaking into my brain, causing pressure and headaches, and that kids who suffered this kind of trauma generally died.

Of course, I didn't die. But when you come close to dying and recover "miraculously," people treat you like a living, breathing miracle. I thrived on that kind of overwhelming positive attention.

And in fact, I had my first spiritual experience in that hospital, one I still remember. My father had been in Vietnam working a construction job, and he took a leave from his contract to come visit me in the pediatric ward. I remember seeing a blue orb-like structure above my bed just as he walked toward me. He didn't see the blue orb, of course, but he remembers being stunned to hear me say, "Dad, I'm not gonna die; I'm here for a reason." Many decades passed before I got a grip on just what that reason might be.

By the time I got to elementary school, the cosmic blue glow had worn off. I felt awkward and different from others, though the intensity of my near-death experience stayed in the back of my mind. I was hyper and impulsive and definitely had learning disabilities—not the best profile for a Catholic-school kid in the mid-1960s. Luckily, I had two champions: my mother, who somehow found the time to help me type school papers, because I couldn't seem to spit my thoughts out onto the page, and Sister Floretta, the incredible teaching nun, who kept me after school in second grade and finally, single-handedly, taught me to read. I was often bored, always disorganized, but there were occasional bright spots—like the day my seventh-grade geography teacher, Ms. Lousie, announced that there were 3.2 billion people in the world, no two alike! "If I work with people," I thought, "I'll never be bored." I was correct.

Just in time for adolescence, I embraced a lifestyle of full-tilt rebellion. At 14, I began using alcohol and marijuana. For a while, I felt like the master of my own destiny, but the year I turned 15, my older brother Ron had his first paranoid schizophrenic break. This meant I had to grow up quickly: my parents needed my help. It was scary and painful to see my brother separated from his true self by a mysterious illness, and because I felt that pain authentically, I pitched in where I could. But it didn't stop my attitude.

My little brother, born the year of my head injury, remembers overhearing a group of priests talking about our family in the halls of the Catholic high school he had just entered. "Oh, no," one of them said, "that's not another Ochoa, is it?" And another priest told him, "Don't worry— that's a smart one."

That's the impression I left—a not-very-smart, rebellious teenager. My little brother went on to be valedictorian of his class. I, needless to say, didn't. He went on to Rice University. I, with my sub-par SAT scores, landed at St. Edwards University because I couldn't get into the University of Texas, my first choice.

I entered college armed with an arsenal of go-to coping mechanisms: methamphetamine, marijuana, alcohol and Colombian coffee, always in interesting combinations. That's how I "medicated" my learning disabilities and my very undiagnosed ADHD, and it worked well enough that I finally got accepted into UT my sophomore year. Somehow I managed to graduate from that school with a degree in psychology and a minor in marketing, with an unimpressive GPA.

The path of my career, in retrospect, is not very path-like. I never got an MD or a PhD. The academic rigor scared me away, and I couldn't make myself look far enough into the future to see a payoff for all that schooling. But I was lucky enough to have a gifted psychology professor who advised me to minor in business if I ever planned to take up psychology for a living.

I wasn't exactly eager to get my graduate degree in counseling. I certainly couldn't hold myself up as an authority on emotional health while using drugs and alcohol in my trademark way. Unwilling to confront that stark reality, I took a job managing a crew of fireplace installers for a few years. It was dull, dependable work, unless you count the day I lost my right ring finger on the job. Or another day—a day off, as it happened—when I narrowly avoided a drug conviction that would have sent me straight to the federal penitentiary. The prospect of losing my freedom (and the reality of losing a body part) woke me up enough to propel me into graduate school, where I finally began to realize that my coping mechanisms weren't working very well anymore—that, like a lot of addicts, I'd self-medicated to the point of over-medication.

And then I met my wife, Edie, at a self-help seminar. I impressed her as "the most egotistical yay-hoo at the seminar, reading poetry, craving attention." We'd been dating for barely six months when she informed me that if I didn't get help for my addictions, she'd leave the relationship. It was a motivational speech, to say the least. I entered my first twelve-step group in 1987, began working toward a graduate degree and started a job at a long-term psychiatric hospital. Eighteen months later, after being attacked by a psychotic teenager, I took a medical leave to work on the resulting post-traumatic stress. For six months, I mowed lawns for $5.25 per hour, doing what I could to prepare for my marriage to Edie, still sober—and cautiously optimistic.

One month after our wedding, I got hired at a summer day treatment program for children with ADHD. I still remember those seven children—the cacophony of their activity and their quirky brilliance. At 26, I was exhausted at the end of a full day's work, but exhilarated, too. Using behavioral-modification techniques, we began to corral the kids' off-the-wall behavior, and their truly unique personalities began to emerge.

I still think about playing a hundred-card sorting game with Josh, aged six. Consistently, he'd find 45 pairs of the 50 that were available. When I asked how he did it, he replied, "I take pictures."

"What do you mean?" "I take pictures of the cards *in my mind.*"

Here was a kid who squirmed in his seat, who would bite and spit on other children when he was angry, but who was also full of life. And who had a *photographic memory*—something we nearly missed because his behavior was usually so out of control as to obscure his true self. I was struck by the realization that these children, living in their own chaotic ADHD worlds, were at risk of losing something very precious: the connection to their unique passions, interests and talents, without which they'd basically just be a set of problem behaviors, to be managed and disciplined.

After a number of years working with ADHD children in a psychiatric hospital, I took a job with adults at a chemical-dependency inpatient program. Many of my clients had serious cocaine addictions to resolve, and while I was ready to help them, I never expected to see some of the same ADHD symptoms I'd seen in the children at my previous job. Remember, this was 1992, when ADHD was seen as almost entirely a "juvenile" syndrome, thought to be outgrown or resolved by adulthood, thanks to medication and behavioral therapy. We were just learning how to treat childhood ADHD effectively, and there was little to no clinical research in the field involving adults. But here were adults acting like...

adults with ADHD. When I asked about their childhood history, many had been diagnosed with, or had had symptoms of, ADHD as children.

I still remember how my clinical mentor reacted when I told him I was thinking about offering ADHD treatment to adults in the chemical-dependency treatment center. "James," he said, "I'm sticking with children. Adults are too complicated. The areas of their life that need help generally include…all of them! I mean, career, relationships, self-esteem, drugs and alcohol. Way too complicated, in my opinion."

Well, not for me. To me, ADHD adults were shiny and interesting. Also, although I didn't yet know it, I was seeing myself in that two-way mirror. Luckily, I was able to find a clinical supervisor who agreed to help me start a four-week adult ADHD education program. We didn't have much help to offer them—not yet—but at least everyone learned something and we all began to get our heads around the idea that, yes, ADHD could persist into adulthood.

After a stint doing addictions treatment at a prison, I was lucky enough to spend four years working for Dr. Byron Kocen, a developmental pediatrician whose office was inundated with ADHD children. While treating them—and learning from Dr. Kocen's invaluable mentorship—I became increasingly aware that a lot of ADHD kids were driven to the office by an ADHD parent. That, in fact, there was such a thing as an adult with ADHD, and that those adults weren't just receptive to the idea of treatment, but also desperate for it.

Up to this point, I never seriously considered that I might have ADHD myself. That changed after I bought a computerized assessment test to use with my clients. At a training, I volunteered to be the guinea pig and take the ADHD assessment, and I made plenty of mistakes, which the psychologist/developer seemed to find amusing. He thought I was "acting" ADHD for the benefit of the class. But I hadn't been trying to miss the targets on purpose! I returned to my seat thinking *Oh, crap, that was really hard for me,* but I wasn't ready to "come out" in front of all the other clinicians.

I showed my results to the test's developer at a national ADHD conference some months later, not mentioning, of course, that they were mine. He said, "This adult is functioning fairly well overall, but there are clear signs of ADHD, all across the board. It's likely creating problems in his life." He was right about that—I struggled with organization, follow-through, writing reports and sequencing. I'd been struggling with those things for years. I had a tough time keeping up with my professional obligations. But I didn't take this opinion as a firm diagnosis. I really wasn't ready to deal with anything that concrete—or sobering.

That's where I was in 1999, when I decided to open my own practice, first known as The ADHD Center, now The Life Empowerment Center. At Dr. Kocen's office, I'd had to schedule between ten and twelve of my own clients each week, and it hadn't been easy. I knew I'd have problems maintaining any kind of clerical system, and yet I still wasn't sure it made sense to hire an administrative assistant. Luckily, when I asked Edie if she thought I needed one, she firmly said, "Yes—you need an assistant." (Not much ambiguity there!)

I ended up hiring Kim to organize me and help me, and she's still here today, thank God. (Kim says, "You're welcome.") But even with an executive assistant and a phone system firmly in place, I was pretty sure I was going to be my own best test case—an adult with ADHD, looking for strategies, solutions and support. So what, exactly, was I going to offer my clients in the way of help? I wondered if anyone would show up at the door of my brand-new practice.

In fact, adults with ADHD showed up, almost immediately. Most of them were very, very happy to have someone to talk to, and I seemed to have a knack for that. Cognitive behavioral-modification techniques were the flavor of the week. Research continues to show their effectiveness in treating ADHD, and it's a good strategy, a good start—but ADHD is complex, and as I came to see, you need more than one strategy to resolve it.

When I used behavioral methods with my clients, my empathy for them grew by leaps and bounds. They were understanding, on an intellectual level, that their brains worked differently, but they just didn't feel good about themselves. Their lives continued to be chaotic, unpredictable and ultimately discouraging. The shame and embarrassment of their ADHD ebbed, flowed and got stuck, over and over again. Ultimately, it isn't possible to think your way out of emotional distress.

Yet initially, most of my clients made progress. Many felt much better, at first, just having a diagnosis—knowing that the way they processed information was legitimately different than the majority of the population. But the emotional undercurrent of distress, the constant missing of details, would knock them out of sync. Eventually, they'd come back to me saying *it's not working. I'm a failure.* I was making a difference for them, but not enough of a difference—and that produced a sense of failure for me, because what I was recommending wasn't sticking in the long term. Time and time again, I'd sit with their frustration: "I can't remember anything! That's not how my brain works! Nobody ever *gets* me! The twenty recommendations I got from my ADHD testing don't make any sense! And how am I supposed to be consistent with them? I haven't been consistent my entire life! Here I am in your office again, and if you can't help me, and *you're the expert,* then I'm truly screwed!"

By the late Nineties, my frustration had organized itself into a few key questions: *How do I give people the emotional sense of self they need to survive the roller-coaster ride of ADHD? Why was that self so damaged in the first place? If it was missing, how could we persuade it to come back?*

I read, pondered, talked with the top researchers in the field and attended their trainings. I experimented with a lot of great theories, but I didn't see much in the way of long-term positive outcome.

And then, because the therapy I was offering wasn't working the way I wanted it to, I decided to try something new. I had known about EMDR (Eye Movement Desensitization and Reprocessing) for about five years, mostly as a successful method of treating trauma and delayed stress. It wasn't necessarily indicated for ADHD, but I had completed a training with the EMDR Institute and become certified (more about those techniques in **Part TWO)**. It was when I finally targeted ADHD symptoms with EMDR that I began to see clients who were getting better and *staying* better.

I'm not saying they were cured, that they walked out my door and disappeared into success-land. Life empowerment involves navigation, and EMDR is just one of the navigational tools I use. It's a very powerful one, though, and it helped me come to terms with what would become the focus of my practice: the Emotional Distress Syndrome of ADHD.

I began to see that the chronic stress of living with ADHD was in many ways similar to the effects of post-traumatic stress disorder. There were definite parallels. People with PTSD experience an event or trauma that is, or is perceived to be, life-threatening. The resulting stress continues to disrupt their lives long after the threat is removed. Emotional triggers set off a re-creation of the past trauma. They have recurring nightmares and flashbacks.

The stress of living with ADHD—the cumulative effects, the fallout—was very similar. A micro-trauma is still a trauma. My clients were struggling with the trauma of a lifetime of failed expectations. They were afraid to take risks, paralyzed, but seemingly had nowhere to turn.

Of course, it wasn't an exact parallel. People being treated for PTSD are usually dealing with a specific trauma, even if it was ongoing in their past, whereas ADHD is a genetic neurological condition, not a single event. To put it another way, EDS comes at us from the inside out, rather than the outside in.

The constant, covert stress of ADHD put us into a chronic state of fight or flight or freeze! And although ADHD was being treated—mostly in kids, and mostly with medication and organizational strategies—the ongoing stress of it was not. It wasn't even being talked about.

Dr. Thomas E. Brown, a clinical and research psychologist at Yale, has a complementary take on the emotional stress of ADHD, reprinted here from his book titled *Smart but Stuck*, with his permission:

"*The role of emotional management in adults with ADHD is something the DSM IV criteria don't touch, but most of us who are clinicians and researchers who deal with adults with ADHD repeatedly encounter patients who have difficulty managing their emotions. For many persons with ADHD, when an emotion hits them, whether it is worry, or they are annoyed about something, or their feelings are hurt, or they begin to feel like they want something very badly, or they are just discouraged about things, that emotion often hits them in the same way a computer virus invades a hard drive: it just gobbles up all of the space inside them, it takes over, and it is really difficult for these patients to put the emotion into perspective and to put it to the back of their minds and get on with what they have to do.*"

What an excellent description of the emotional distress caused by ADHD. That's my story. Now it's time to talk about yours.

YOU AND YOUR ADHD

I assume you're reading this because you have attention problems, as they're sometimes called. And maybe sometimes you wonder—or someone asks you to wonder—if attention problems aren't just part of the human condition. It's a good question. In fact, it's a common belief, in this fast-paced world, that *everyone* has attention problems.

I see the point: To some degree or other, everyone goes through periods where stress is exponential and focusing is hard. But people with ADHD go through it more often, and the repeated episodes of distress build into wicked cycles.

It's like the proverbial snowball rolling downhill—if the snowball picked up all kinds of debris along the way. Branches, trees, small animals, abandoned buildings, other people's entire lives… Excuse the messy metaphor, but, as you probably know all too well, this can be a messy, chaotic way to live.

In other words, stress is everywhere, but contrary to popular belief, everyone in the world can't claim to have ADHD. (Why they'd want to is a whole 'nother question!) More like three to five percent of the population, and that's according to the most conservative of many estimates. The more liberal end of the spectrum says that ten percent of us have this particular neurological condition.

So is it real, or what?

Spoiler alert: Yes. ADHD is real.

The research, especially in recent years, has made it quite clear that this constellation of symptoms is an inherited, neurological condition. But since I'm not a scientist, and since neuroscientists are probably learning something new about ADHD as I'm writing this, I won't attempt a detailed explanation of the ADHD brain.

Instead, I'll draw this picture in very broad strokes.

The brain of a person with ADHD may have a smaller-than-average prefrontal cortex, the part of the brain that regulates planning, evaluating, delaying gratification, focusing, doing more than one thing at a time—all those processes we find so challenging. And the connection between the prefrontal cortex and the dopamine receptors appears not to be as efficient as it could be. (Dopamine is a neurotransmitter that controls the brain's ability to get motivated and experience pleasure, among other nice things.) So, the "reward circuitry" of a person with ADHD may be interrupted, slowed down, otherwise less efficient.

Perhaps to compensate, the limbic system, the primeval part of the brain that perceives threat and acts on adrenaline—the fight, flight or freeze part—seems to be overactive in the ADHD brain. So the nervous, stressed, caveman-running-from-a-mastodon instinct is overactive. And the part that prioritizes and plans ahead is underactive.

That's how I understand the science of ADHD.

And here's my interpretive version: The prefrontal cortex of a person with ADHD cannot rest easily or often in the details of life. Because its reward circuitry is interrupted and/or incomplete, there's no incentive for it to finish what it starts. Instead, it wanders around in search of something shiny, something to galvanize its attention. When it lights up or engages fully, its efficiency can quickly become obsessive. Adding a column of tax figures would not light it up. Working a wickedly difficult Sudoku puzzle just might.

PUT THIS ON YOUR REFRIGERATOR

ADHD is a brain-based difference.

It has nothing to do with intelligence. It is not possible to rewire your brain through intelligence or willpower.

Structure works.

Routines and systems: create them, trust them, use them.

It's not natural to plan, prioritize, or think ahead.

If it is not done very deliberately, it will not happen.

Without meaning, it won't get done.

Your attention is selective; it has to deem something interesting to stay focused.

Take personal responsibility for your ADHD.

Although ADHD may explain certain behaviors, it is not an excuse for them.

Distractions are everywhere, all the time.

Learning to manage your ADHD is the only way to fight distractions.

Your brain craves stimulus.

Creating a dramatic situation by waiting until the last minute to meet a deadline is one way to give your brain the stimulation it craves, but maybe not the smartest way.

Engineer the environment.

Learn how to create a personalized, ADHD-friendly environment that works for you.

Break it down.

If something feels big, make it small by zeroing in on the very next action you could take that will move this task forward. Move from that next action to the next-next action. Make these "next actions" as small as they need to be to feel manageable.

Try a decathlon approach to fitness.

Reduce fitness monotony by identifying ten different physical activities to keep you motivated. With that many options to choose from, you're unlikely to ever be too bored to exercise.

How Does It Feel to Have ADHD?

As those who have lived with, worked with or fallen in love with someone diagnosed with ADHD know, there's just something different about ADHD-ers. After two decades of observing myself and others, I've gotten a pretty clear picture of how it feels to live life with ADHD.

Different. Weird. Out of sync. People who don't have ADHD, "regular" people, don't seem to have trouble doing things that strike us as very, very difficult. That could be because at some point in their early to mid-twenties, their non-ADHD brains underwent a maturing process. So if they simply focus on remembering a task, it's likely to not get forgotten! (Can you imagine?)

Non-ADHD wisdom is full of trying harder, sucking it up, going back to the old drawing board, pulling yourself up by the bootstraps. These slogans can be very helpful, I hear. Unless you have ADHD—in which case your bootstraps snapped years ago, and you're still trying to pull yourself up using that invention you almost-but-not-quite got around to patenting, the thing with the pulleys. If only you could remember where you put those drawings...

If you're part of the three to five percent, your view of the world is skewed, from just about every vantage point. Organization, follow-through, vision, clarity, communication—all just a little out of step with what you experience going on around you. You're constantly thinking of what's either behind or ahead of where you are right now, ping-ponging backward and forward in time. The ADHD brain seems to shift gears a few beats early. It has trouble *settling down* in the present, particularly if the present contains a lot of details. There's a persistent restlessness, a neurological hum. You can't always commit—to a conversation, a thought, a relationship. You *want* to commit, but you also feel compelled to fidget or fiddle or pace, just to keep your mind engaged. Someone asks *Are you paying attention?* You say *Of course.* You hope you are, anyway.

Prognosis: Good News and Bad News

Now imagine that you not only have the inherited, genetic condition known as ADHD, but a few other strikes against you. Say you're growing up in poverty, or with a weak family system, or in an educational system that doesn't have time to understand how best to teach you. Or with mental illness or addiction—in your genes and/or your surroundings. Now the constant misplacing of keys or reading glasses, on top of everything else, can start to feel downright unmanageable. And those are just everyday, private annoyances, right? Wrong. Unfortunately, your ADHD isn't just about you. Other people are affected by the actions of your scattered brain. Maybe sometimes you'd like to live alone, in a vacuum, but it's not possible.

The short version is this: ADHD is no joke, and you ignore it at your peril. Untreated, unmanaged ADHD is a quick path to neurological chaos.

It can be more than frustrating to go through life this way. The frustration can morph into serious discouragement. The discouragement can grow into a sense that life is a matter of unrelenting struggle.

But having ADHD can also be very stimulating. It can be fun. I mean it. Imagine a stone skipping across the surface of a lake, and now imagine being that stone! You can't seem to get below the surface of the water, but what you're doing feels close to flying, and somehow that heightened sensation feels more normal than risky. You may not know how to plan your day, but you do know how to entertain yourself. That's a rare skill. Give yourself credit.

ADHD adults are constantly looking for stimulation, whether or not they do it consciously. This can drive their loved ones and bosses crazy, or impress them with out-of-the-box thinking or finding answers that others don't.

Under the right circumstances, being one of the three to five percent can feel special. You're a rare jewel, blessed with the ability to see the big picture, while others bog down in daily details. But I wouldn't get too attached to the buzz you get from this particular feeling, as it tends to be fleeting. And more often, living with ADHD is a series of significant challenges.

So the truth is that there are strikes against you, and it does little good to ignore the truth. On the other hand, if that's the only angle from which you see your ADHD, it will suck the life right out of you. What I'm saying is this: You have a serious responsibility to come to terms with your brain chemistry.

So how do you do that?

Knowledge is power. It starts with a diagnosis.

Diagnosis

The first step is making an appointment with a licensed professional counselor with long-term ADHD expertise or a psychiatrist MD, or signing up for a full psychological evaluation. You'll probably be asked for an incredibly detailed life history—likely more than once. You'll fill out assessment checklists, and you'll bring home checklists for your friends and family to complete. You might take a visual and auditory attention assessment, a test my clients have described as both "nothing short of neurological torture" and "a series of boring, routine and monotonous tasks that becomes meaningless in 30 seconds, but you have to do it for 16 minutes." (I take this test myself every six months or so, just to keep my compassion in good working order.)

After these assessments, you may return with a new label: Attention Deficit Hyperactivity Disorder, perhaps with a subheading such as "primarily inattentive," "hyperactive/impulsive" and the like. (Whichever it is, the Emotional Distress Syndrome is likely to be an equal-opportunity offender.) ADHD is a term that makes sense in the linear world, and there's nothing wrong with that. Society uses all kinds of frames, roles and definitions. But in many ways, it's also an unfortunate term, full of connotations of...deficit! And disorder! Just hearing yourself identified with this label can make you feel worse about yourself than you already do.

On one hand, you're so emotionally relieved to have an explanation for the way your mind works. On the other hand, should you tell people? What if they don't believe you or support you? The key, I think, is to find a functional way to talk about ADHD, and in order to do that, you need a functional way to think about it—*to have the conversation with yourself before you begin it with your friends and family.*

At this point, all reputable ADHD books tell you to go out and learn everything you can about "the condition." There's a reason for that: Simply understanding that your brain works differently helps most of us feel less crazy.

I'd say spend as little time as possible in the deficit and disorder of it all and give yourself every chance to progress ahead to *how do I support my brain? How do I figure out what works for me?* The more you understand your ADHD brain, the better you'll be able to calm the distress of learning you have it.

Coming Out of the ADHD Closet

At some point during this process, you may find yourself sharing information with someone who is less than receptive, who puts you on the wrong end of a weary glance. Sooner or later, you'll get the all-too-common questions and comments:

- ADHD isn't real.

- Isn't it something they came up with to medicate regular, rowdy kids?

- Wasn't it invented by the pharmaceutical industry?

- You're faking a diagnosis to try and score drugs.

- You should just snap out of it.

- And the ever-popular YOU SHOULD JUST TRY HARDER!

It's easier said than done, but try not to get lost in the knee-jerk reactions. For the most part, people aren't trying to hurt you. You may be able to teach them something they don't know—though maybe not now, when you're still getting used to your diagnosis.

Or if you just want a short answer to the ever-present question—*Is ADHD real?*—here's one you can use:

> *Yes. ADHD is real. It's not a virus. It's a neurological and developmental condition, as genetically coded as hair color and height.*

If you want a longer answer, and you'll allow me a moment of indignation, try this:

> *How many other diagnoses are so chronically debated, in such an insidious way? We don't debate diabetes—that's a genetic issue, right? Well, ADHD is a genetic issue, too. I can't change how short or tall you are, and I can't change having been born with this.*

Grief and Relief: the Roller Coaster

As you gain understanding of your diagnosis, the untethered loose ends of your life knit together into what looks like a unified whole. You begin to perceive explanations for behaviors and events in your past that didn't make sense at the time. And then suddenly, just as you feel downright capable, you're overwhelmed with a feeling of being pulled out to sea. It's bad enough to suddenly be so aware of time lost that can never be regained, of bridges burned—but now this loss of emotional control? What the heck????

"When I was a kid, we didn't have ADD. We had "John doesn't apply himself." I was told to try harder. Stay on task. Listen closer. "You can do anything you put your mind to." Well that sorta worked for a while. But when I found that I couldn't do what I put my mind to, like save my dad or my marriage, my whole self image came apart, and I acted out in ways that were not consistent with the person I was raised to be. I became angry. I became a yeller. A cynic."

Then, as suddenly as it came on, the feeling subsides, and you're back on shore, safe and sound, thinking, *Okay, I'll regroup, learn about this ADHD, come up with some personalized strategies for managing it and*...WHAM, another tidal wave on the horizon! Stay with it. Set a timer. It won't last as long as you think it will.

"I wasn't aware I even had ADD. I wasn't the typical hyper child. As an adult, I found myself not able to even work effectively. I lost a job because I just couldn't focus and do the work that I had tried to motivate myself to do in a lot of different ways. I was ashamed, desperate, depressed, and frustrated. I didn't know what to do about the problem. I didn't know how to talk about it with other people. I felt a lot like my fellow soldiers as they returned from Afghanistan, but for completely different reasons. After being diagnosed with ADHD, I was immediately more calm. Knowing that I didn't merely have an unassailable character flaw was immensely helpful. Knowing that there were biological reasons for the way I saw my life slip over the years was comforting. Finding out these crucial things allowed me to peer through the mists and see the problems generating the fog. Being able to focus on those problems and find ways to manage them has been incredibly empowering."

Grief and relief come with the territory. If you're feeling both, you're not alone. Relax, and let's talk about this. (You can always panic later.)

Grief goes hand in hand with second-guessing, with a deep sense of wasted time and missed opportunities.

- What if I had known this about myself ten years ago?
- Would I have lost my first marriage?
- Could I have followed through with my million-dollar idea?

And then comes relief. Because, really, it's comforting to have an explanation for the weirdness that is, and has been, you. At the very least, this knowledge calms the limbic survival instinct of your brain, which as you now know, is probably a little more active than it should be.

What to do with the grief and relief of it all?

After diagnosis comes treatment.

Medication

Often, but not always, ADHD is treated with medication. Depending on the severity of their situation, I sometimes advise my clients to seek a medication evaluation from a psychiatrist, particularly if there are complicating factors such as depression or anxiety. I've also had clients whose medication was easily managed by a primary care physician. Either way, I think it's important to understand what meds can, and cannot, help with. Finding the right meds is a very individualized, ongoing process. And by "meds," I don't just mean Western prescription drugs, because herbal remedies, naturopathic tinctures, nutritional supplements and exercise have helped some of my clients over the years, with a success rate about equal to that of traditional prescriptions.

All the same, I'm not sure why Western medications—all of Western medicine, in fact—have become so suspect. Some people just have a knee-jerk negative reaction when I bring up the subject. I always assure patients who feel this way that Western medicine is just one end of the treatment spectrum. Its practitioners strive to treat whatever's unbalanced or diseased in the body. That approach has saved us from infection and intervened in serious illnesses. But Western views aren't always balanced— in fact, they can be out of balance. An intense medical intervention can have significant transformational effects, as well as significant side effects. Chemotherapy, for example. Let's just know that that's true.

But let's also remember that Western medical treatment closes the gap of ADHD symptoms the fastest. In most cases, when you're talking about medications for ADHD, you eventually talk about stimulants— Adderall, Vyvanse and the like. There are people who think the medications themselves are the problem. They're not perfect, and not everyone can take them, but I hesitate to call them the problem. Ideally, they do a very good job of improving concentration. In many cases, people feel an almost instantaneous relief, a lightening of the load. The research shows that they work really well.

A few of my clients have been happily stable on one prescription for years. Some need their dosages and medications regularly tweaked. Others can't tolerate the side effects, or find that they outweigh the benefits. Still others won't take stimulants in the first place: they let their beliefs or fears push the possibility away.

Also, there are patterns that aren't very well explained by the research. For some people, the drugs will become less effective—a phenomenon that's true for all medications, actually. In these cases, finding the "right" meds is an ongoing project, as new medications for ADHD (stimulants and otherwise) continue to come on the market. There's no one solution, and everyone's an individual, especially when it comes to how you metabolize and react to pharmaceuticals.

The whole question of medication gets so complicated and obfuscated that it's easy to lose sight of the reality: ADHD is a genetic condition, and there's some very good science on how to manage genetics. Not to trust hard science is a little bit silly, I think.

Stimulants are a good example: They've been studied far more than any other class of drug, possibly because there's a very real concern about the connection between stimulants and addiction. But the research shows that people with untreated ADHD are more likely to develop addiction problems and that this risk is mitigated when ADHD is treated with a stimulant! To put it another way, it's been well established that stimulant medication can help people with addictions to be less addict-like.

Now, if you have a history of abusing stimulants or any other substance, it's clearly more complicated. Stimulant meds may not be out of the question for you, but you have to be really honest—not just with your clinician, but with yourself. It bears repeating: You really need to have a thorough evaluation with a trained physician. It's not something you can guess at.

And then, once you're taking these medications, it's equally important to collaborate with your doctor, so that you're involved in the process as much as your doctor is, giving constant feedback.

My Own Experience with Medication

I come to the table with over 25 years of recovery and a predisposition for addiction that runs in my family. My drug-and-alcohol days ended a long time ago, but they're a good example of the things people do to address undiagnosed ADHD—in my case, a self-medication program of marijuana and methamphetamine.

Seeing the positive way my clients reacted to prescribed stimulants made me want to try them myself, and I did, a few times, with my family doctor, but found they kicked off my cravings. At one point, my doctor prescribed a very low dose of Adderall that helped my focus and concentration but also pushed some old buttons— why else would I have felt the need to add three to four Venti-sized Starbucks coffees each day? Edie was rightly concerned, even as I assured her, in rapid-fire speech, *I'm-fine-I-can-handle-this-don't-worry-about-it!* I couldn't handle it, of course. To make a long story short, stimulant medications didn't seem to be an option for me, and

I went back to managing my ADHD with therapy, strategies and, it must be admitted, plenty of caffeine and energy drinks.

Fast-forward ten years. My older son Gabe, then a student at Georgia Tech, began having academic challenges. Gabe was, by any standard, a very accomplished young man. He'd always been smart; he'd always had excess energy. At age two, he watched me use a screwdriver and then took a cabinet door off its hinges! And now, at this prestigious college, his restlessness seemed to be catching up with him. When I sent him to an Austin colleague for psychological testing, the findings were fascinating: ADHD, hyperactive-impulsive type, plus a wickedly high IQ. It seemed Gabe had been able to use his intelligence and self-designed strategies to work around the more complex details of his life for many years, but the rigor of one of the top engineering schools in the country had overwhelmed him. He started on an extended-release version of Ritalin that hadn't been considered the last time I tried medication. Gabe did so well that I shared his story with my personal psychiatrist, a doctor I've known professionally for twenty years, a person with whom I've been completely honest about my addiction history. After discussing my addiction response, we decided to see how I did on a low dose of Concerta.

It's now been over two years, and this medication is still working well for me. My planning and prioritizing and thinking are on a much more even keel.

But—and this is important—medication is not the only tool I use to manage my ADHD. I couldn't achieve any kind of balance if it were. Medication is not the only trick in the book (or *this* book!).

To sum up, research suggests that medication is a very effective intervention for the treatment of ADHD. It also suggests, just as strongly, that it can't be the *only* intervention. Beyond education, strategies and emotional and spiritual development, you'll often have to consider other ways to work with your neurochemistry.

A perfect example of this would be taking a long, hard look at your nutrition. What, exactly, are you putting into your body? You might end up working with a nutritionist or an herbologist or starting on a program of supplements and vitamins. Over the years, there's been medical research done about the inter-relation of nutrition and ADHD—in particular, the role of sugar, food additives and protein—but results, so far, are all anecdotal. Understandably, people are looking for a magic bullet: *If I stop eating sugar, maybe my symptoms will disappear.*

And if you do happen to find a magic bullet, don't be surprised if its mojo wears off. Most of us need regular tune-ups from the medication specialist on our team. Some of my clients have begun phasing off medication after more than a decade. Others are having their first positive experiences with meds, decades after diagnosis.

It comes back to acceptance: In the search for the right meds, or the right alternative to meds, you must accept yourself lock, stock and barrel, brain chemistry, warts and all. Blaming your ADHD brain chemistry—or blaming the "normal" people who don't always get you—doesn't help.

Or, as they say, it's an explanation, not an excuse.

Coaching, Therapy, Helpful Advice

You have the meds. You have the diagnosis. Maybe you signed up for a newsletter from CHADD (Children and Adults with ADHD, the largest of the national support groups). You're actively engaged in the process of self-help. Good for you. Do you still need to see somebody? To hire a *confidante*, coach, friend?

My answer is a qualified yes. Read on.

Most of us are familiar with the concept of psychotherapy. Often, adults who end up in my office have a long and storied background in some kind of talk therapy—anything from the logic-oriented Cognitive Behavioral Therapy, to Jung's archetypes, to the myriad other portals into consciousness. I'm almost always grateful for the background and insight that comes along with those years of self-examination, whether or not the ADHD was addressed or even acknowledged.

In my practice, I use an educational, directive, action-oriented approach. I don't sit on the sidelines very long before making suggestions and throwing out ideas for personalized strategies. For me, this method is the best way to manage and treat ADHD long-term. I've also had very encouraging results with EMDR (Eye Movement Desensitization and Reprocessing). The therapist or practitioner who clicks for you might use different methods or subscribe to different ideologies, which is fine, as long as you work well together.

And that's the thing: If your life is out of control, it can be enormously helpful to find a therapist you trust and get to work. If you're the type of person who's had trouble expressing emotion, therapy can help you work through the hesitancy and fear. If you're carrying around historical family baggage, a therapist's office is a good place to unpack those bags and sort through them. If you're having trouble with a key relationship, a therapist can be the best kind of mediator—almost a translator.

ADHD alone usually gives people plenty to discuss. It's important, though, that the therapist recognizes the ADHD and the neurochemistry that goes along with it. If not, a lot of time can be wasted and a lot of ground can be lost; there has to be more to talk therapy than just expressing the frustrations that come with the condition. ADHD clients who don't realize any benefit from therapy, for whatever reason, can see it as a personal failure, which is always a lousy outcome. If the therapist just didn't take the time to understand the ADHD, it's a downright tragedy.

Coaching—a sort of down-to-earth adjunct to therapy—is often recommended as part of ADHD treatment. Coaching is basically a positive psychology that starts with the premise that you're okay, and that your coach is less an academic expert than a teacher, or an advocate, in *your* corner, rooting for *you*. It's a forward-looking model. Together, you and your coach figure out where you are now, where you want to be in the future, and how to get there.

The term "coaching" is simply more acceptable to a lot of people. You may feel a stigma about seeing a therapist, as if that implies something's wrong with your brain or your emotions. And in fact, coaches aren't trained to revisit the past to process emotional history the way therapists do. We all want to think we can learn or be taught as opposed to being broken or diseased and in need of repair. Coaches have been normalized as people who bring out the best in you, who stand on the sidelines and cheer you on. This can be very useful for ADHD adults—especially when their self-esteem hits bottom.

Take the familiar issue of losing your car keys. In a perfect world, a coach would also give you a good grounding in how your brain works—what happens in your short-term memory that causes you to misplace things. Then he or she would help you come up with a half-dozen strategies for how not to lose those keys. Keeping the keys in a dish on top of the stove, for instance, because after all, you cook breakfast every morning, just before getting into the car and driving to work. After a while, you no longer feel awkward or strange using such strategies, and the next time a strategic challenge comes up, the coach can say, *Hey, remember what you did with your car keys?*

A personalized strategy can be as simple as choosing a rollerball pen because the positive feeling of the ink flowing onto the page makes it easier to accomplish a required writing task. It could involve hiring executive and/or organizational assistance whenever you can afford it. As an adult with ADHD, there's almost no facet of your life that couldn't benefit from being custom-tailored to your personality. (For example, what kind of music do you listen to while working or studying? None? Heavy metal? Ambient electronica? If so, the Beethoven symphony that helps someone else focus might have the opposite effect on you.)

As a clinician-slash-therapist-slash-coach, my goal is always to teach people as much as I possibly can about how the brain works to produce insight and action. First you learn, then you develop personalized strategies that tap into the ways you learn best. This is where my clients begin to reach *aha* points, where they think, *Okay, this isn't how other people do it, but it works for me.*

What I hope my clients get from me, or any coach, is a functional perspective—a way to harness their imagination and creativity in the service of order and clarity in their lives.

Over the past twenty years, I've evaluated countless different coaching systems—partly because it's important to be informed, but also because, as a fellow ADHD-er, I absolutely relate to the search for something newer and better. Shinier, if you will. The eternal struggle to get and stay organized is important, but also boring, and once we experience a little relief, our minds tend to wander off to something a little more…fascinating.

So when it comes to choosing strategies and systems, we can be fickle. I admit it.

One concept that's stood the test of time for me is David Rock's Results Coaching System (www.resultscoaches.com). This type of executive coaching may have been designed for businesspeople, not necessarily with any ADHD component, but it comes from a place of vision, planning and goal setting. Because the people I work with are often just starting to reach their potential, I appreciate the way Results Coaching methods help them to focus on dreams and aspirations. There's more to life, in other words, than how to organize your closet or stop aggravating your loved ones.

Whatever ADHD coach or coaching system appeals to you, it should be flexible and personalize-able. In the beginning, you won't always know what kinds of methods fit you, and that out-of-ideas feeling may leave you discouraged. To that end, I'll sit with people and help them discover how relatively weak or strong they are in all the areas that matter. I'll help them understand how ADHD has affected their abilities. Really understanding how their brain responds takes the recrimination out of it: It doesn't mean they're broken, but it could mean their solutions might look unusual to others.

Somehow, just knowing that can calm you down.

Which is good.

And it can be a big relief to lay the disarray of your big, messy life at someone's feet and let them help you untangle it and keep track of it.

Which is also good.

But?

Yes, there's a *but*. Because although you can and should form a treatment team to help you handle your ADHD, all the meds and personalized strategies in the world won't help you handle the emotional distress of the condition.

In other words, we've come to the end of the ADHD 101 part of this book. ADHD 101 will only take you so far.

It's time to venture out into The Storm.

PART TWO

WEATHERING THE STORM

Think of the storm roaming the sky
uneasily like a dog looking for a place
to sleep in, listen to it growling.
—Elizabeth Bishop

There's so much helpful information for people with ADHD—about medication and diagnoses, about how to get things done, or finish faster, or feel more confident about your decisions. All good information. The problem is that we can't really use it until we confront the fallout from the emotional stress of life as an ADHD adult. And to confront that emotional stress, we have to look at it, to acknowledge its existence. And who wants to do that, when the mind's natural instinct is to fight, run off somewhere shiny and exciting, or freeze?

When I introduced my clients to the EDS concept, they *got* it. Emotional Distress Syndrome. Hell, they were living it. They didn't feel confident, despite their Ph.Ds and bank balances and successful careers— and still, unless you're having an abject breakdown or failure, it's hard to look at the role emotional distress has played in your life, the havoc it's still creating, and the prospect of what will happen if it continues unchecked.

It's hard to look at. Let's look at it anyway.

WHAT IS THE STORM?

A favorite client remembers her mental state—a sort of perma-Storm—when she first entered my practice:

> "I have a hard time starting things, getting things accomplished, keeping track of time, prioritizing what actually needs to be done. Typical ADHD stuff. And I have always been so frustrated with myself about it. My head used to have a constant stream of things like: "Why can't you just do it?" "Why can't you do it RIGHT?" "That was so stupid!" "When are you ever going to figure this out?" I would see the frustration in those around me. I was always trying to explain that I was sorry, that I knew they were frustrated, that YES, I did get it and "trust me, however much you are frustrated with me, I guarantee I'm even more frustrated with myself!" At times it got so overwhelming that I would go into these downward depression spirals that often ended with me crying on the floor of the bathroom, asking my husband why he put up with me and inwardly wondering why I was even alive. The spirals didn't happen often, but the pattern was consistent. I can't attribute all of this to EDS—some comes from childhood trauma and a family history of depression, but the inability to change my patterns led to an incredible sense of worthlessness, pain and borderline suicidal depression."

Here's another client, a very different person, describing the familiar dread of knowing she's on the verge of another Storm:

> "It's like I was born with a small, sharp pebble in my shoe. I can never get this pebble out. Sometimes I find shoes that fit better, or

I get in better shape and somehow walk better, or the pebble shifts and becomes a little less annoying, or it forms a callus. But then I'm just walking along and out of nowhere, there's a sharp pain, and the blister rips open and once again I wonder WHAT IS WRONG WITH ME? Look at all the other people, running and walking and skipping! Look at me, feeling sorry for myself! Why can't I just walk through the pain? Why am I so impaired? I'm sitting here crying—who would believe me if I told them the truth, that I'm crying because I can't get this pebble out of my shoe?"

So how does this Emotional Distress Syndrome play out in people's lives? What *is* the storm?

The cycle goes something like this:

1. Something irritates/overwhelms/startles you.

- You run out of gas on the way home from work, and when you look for your AAA card, you discover your wallet is missing.

- Your teenage daughter, who was supposed to be spending the night with a close family friend, turns out to have spent the night somewhere else entirely. You don't know where she is, whether she's safe or whether she'll survive the angry outburst you'll deliver the minute you find out she's still alive.

- An interoffice e-mail informs you that another round of layoffs is coming.

- You don't like the look of that mole. It looks like skin cancer. You get it tested. It's benign.

- It's malignant.

- A dear friend commits suicide.

- Your wife asks if you made that call you were going to make.

- Your dad says something Dad-like: "What's the *matter* with you?"

- Someone says something, maybe not even directed at you: "What are you, stupid?"

- Wow, you look so fat in that picture. In your opinion. Really, really fat.

- You should have changed the batteries in the smoke alarm months ago. Now you can't find the batteries you bought, and all the alarms are beeping.

- You owe $45,000 in taxes this year. No, it's not a typo.

YOU HAVE ADHD. THIS IS THE SINGLE MOST DISRUPTIVE FACTOR. Because your brain's limbic system sees all the items listed above as threats and reacts accordingly.

In short, something *gets to you*. Later on, after the storm has subsided, you might be able to trace the precipitating problem to your ADHD, to discover how you jumped to a skewed conclusion. But you don't make those connections in real time. You really can't—you're not really thinking clearly. At times like these, you're not very analytical, to put it mildly.

2. Your brain shifts into survival mode.

- You yell, you fume, you react, or

- You cry, or

- You shut down, you disappear, you hole up, or

- You become very oversensitive. Emotions seem to leave bruises.

- Your thinking goes foggy, you can't focus on what's in front of you, you get lost on your way to a familiar destination, or

- You ruminate, perseverate, obsess, dabble in obsessive-compulsive disorder.

- Although you think and think and think, a gear has slipped. Somehow you're unable to draw a conclusion or make a plan. Or just *stop thinking, already.*

Ninety-nine percent of my clients come here for the first time locked firmly in survival mode, marinating in a toxic juice of self-loathing and second-guessing. Some are uncontrollably weepy. Some get defensive—protecting their boundaries any way they can. Some seem to be in a state of lockdown. At first, it can be very difficult to get through to them.

At least I can sympathize. I've been there. It's the neurological hum in the background, the overactive repetition in the mind, the careening anxiety, the waiting for the bad consequences of the bad actions, real or imagined, to land and sink in their talons.

3. The feelings are bad, so you try to make them go away.

- You eat or drink or snort or swallow…something.

- You find a messiah, a person, a theory or a system to follow, as blindly as possible.

- You sleep a lot, or not at all.

- You change jobs, spouses, cities, wardrobes, cars or religions.

Your efforts yield results, but not necessarily helpful ones. The shininess of the new wears off, you run out of luck or money. The bad feelings may go away, but not for long.

4. You search for someone to blame. You find the villain. It's you.

It's you. Your self. You're flawed. You're worthless. No matter what you try, you end up here, again. You can sabotage any system ever imagined, turn any sweet substance into rotting garbage. Those who recognized your potential or encouraged you to persevere are all idiots. As, of course, are you.

What a message!

You play and replay it. You'd think you'd get tired of it. No such luck.

In fact, there's something weirdly comforting about this repeating tape loop. It almost calms you down to think these familiar thoughts, nasty and negative though they are.

5. Eventually, the storm subsides, leaving damage in its wake.

Maybe you find a new therapist or a new medication. Sad to say, though, not all medicine is good medicine. Perhaps some practitioner says, *Here, take this pill, everything will be okay.* Or some coach says, *Here, take this laminated list of strategies—everything will be fine.* When those suggestions fail, it's hard to think anything will work. Each miracle that fails to materialize leaves a little scar, a little ding.

More commonly, a storm subsides on its own, in its own time, and you never really know why. You remind yourself that apparently no storm, not even yours, goes on forever.

—————— The Emotional Distress Syndrome ——————

The Emotional Distress Syndrome (EDS) *is the cumulative effect of the neurological processing differences and behavioral challenges associated with ADHD.* It's a chronic state of emotional stress directly related to the struggle to live life with ADHD, a stress that breaks down emotional tolerance, stamina and the ability to maintain a strong sense of well-being and spiritual health. The chronic, lifelong nature of ADHD-related stress can increase to such a level that it becomes a syndrome akin to post-traumatic stress disorder (PTSD).

As with other ADHD symptoms, there's good news and bad news, and you have choices to make:

- It won't disappear on its own. One way or another, you'll have to manage your emotional distress for the rest of your life.
- If you choose not to manage the emotional distress, the EDS will continue to erode your sense of emotional, mental and physical well-being.
- The Emotional Distress Syndrome *can* be managed.
- You're not broken.
- You can live a full, interesting, potential-reaching life.

I'll repeat that: You can live a full, interesting, potential-reaching life.

There will always be storms. Even if your meds are working fantastically well and nothing is outwardly broken in your life, the emotional part of you still needs shoring up. You need more—more than meds, more than a consistent schedule—to tolerate the inevitable inconsistency. Things will go out of balance, and if you feel lousy every time they do, that's just too much vulnerability.

I now know that it's possible to break through permanent survival mode, to use internal strength to calm myself in the midst of a storm. In other words, I know it's possible to thrive.

Maybe, like my newer clients, you're skeptical. You might think thriving is a matter of luck, and you don't see yourself as lucky. You might think that in order to function, you have to win the lottery. But even lottery winners can still be at enormous emotional risk because of the way they feel about themselves. How many multi-millionaires still fear that the world sees them as a fraud, or that they got where they are because of an undeserved break?

That's still survival thinking. It's not thriving.

Thriving is different. It's about the ability to know yourself, to understand how you operate, how you organize things, what you're good at and what you need help with. Thriving begins with getting connected to yourself. You can get used to thriving. You can even have fun thriving! You can discover your God-given imagination, for instance, and marvel at its elegance and sense of humor.

Imagine how it would feel to thrive through a typically overbooked day, through all the typical complications, with your own unique and sometimes underactive ADHD brain chemistry. Really, what would that be like?

Well, it wouldn't mean that things had calmed down once and for all.

It wouldn't mean that the universe had handed you a time management app that magically estimated exactly how long it takes to do grocery shopping for a household of four without forgetting anything on your list.

It wouldn't mean that you had finally figured out how to color-code, though if color-coding works for you, knock yourself out.

In short, thriving isn't the same thing as being organized or getting your life under control or implementing ADHD-friendly strategies, though all those things are valuable. Thriving is deeper, and it happens on a deeper emotional level.

It might feel like this:

"After encountering the concept of the Emotional Distress Syndrome, I was able to acknowledge in therapy how much I felt like a screw-up, for so many years, that I just couldn't do anything right. From there, I could see how those years of self-doubt, self-criticism and frustration took a toll on my self-esteem and self-worth. This acknowledgement led me to understand the patterns going on in my head and I was able to change them. In my case, a great deal of healing came quickly.

Before, when I was unable to sort out how to proceed with something, which of my list of urgent issues to address first, I would freeze in panic, wonder why my heart was racing and then spiral downward. Now, just knowing what factors are at play allows me to make the connections (at ADHD-speed!) as I feel the tension, frustration, fear and panic arise. And with those connections comes the understanding that it's "just" the EDS. Not to minimize the severity of EDS in any way, but acknowledging what I am experiencing allows me to diffuse the downward panic spiral and stop it in its tracks! Instead of being panicked by the fact that I'm freaked out, I can use my tools to address it."

Thriving isn't a magical ability. In fact, you can *learn* to thrive, and that is exactly what I'm excited to teach you. I hope to help you build, and then strengthen, a solid sense of yourself.

The work ahead of you is all about building this inner strength, and I do mean *building*, because people with ADHD come with structural problems. They may have once used their ADHD to function, to see above the problem, to get the *oh-crap-it's-due-tomorrow-at-6am-and-now-it's-11pm* paper written at the last minute, but they can't seem to pull it off anymore. Even when they appear outwardly confident, their inner strength has been eroded and compromised by the continual stress of the Emotional Distress Syndrome.

But it's possible to build, or rebuild, a strong foundation, and from a strong foundation, you can actually reach for things. Courage, confidence and the ability to take risks all depend on a strong foundation.

Specifically, *two strong pillars:*

SELF-ESTEEM AND SELF-IDENTITY

Ideally, these pillars are present within us at birth, growing along with us, offering support and strength. Ideally, these pillars are built from unconditional love and positive regard—by which I mean that the most significant people in your life demonstrate, beyond the shadow of a doubt, that they love you and believe in you. Not that they expect you to be exempt from hardship, but that you'll be resilient. That whatever comes, you'll be able to embrace life and reap its rewards.

Ideally.

But maybe your childhood wasn't ideal. Maybe you're not an ideal parent. It's okay. That's where the rebuilding comes in.

One Pillar at a Time

Let's start with a concept you've probably heard a lot about but may not see entirely clearly.

Here's my take.

Self-esteem is your inner-driven sense of your innate value as a person, separate from any way in which you're viewed, evaluated or otherwise defined in the outside world. Having self-esteem means a commitment to finding meaning in your life, to the belief that you deserve happiness and fulfillment. It's believing and demonstrating that caring for yourself is a worthwhile pursuit, even when it's not easy.

Perhaps you've gotten the message that cultivating self-esteem is a selfish, even narcissistic, pursuit. If so, try to let that message go, because there's no reason not to be on your own side. Think of the old airline safety speech: You have to put on your own oxygen mask before you can help others with theirs.

There is, or ought to be, something unconditional about self-esteem. Some people experience it as unconditional self-love, others more as unconditional acceptance of where they are and what is happening at any particular moment, in the moment. Self-esteem is what makes you able to hold your own hand, to be there for yourself in a spirit of moral support.

Self-esteem is the measure of your love, care and concern for your own welfare. How well do you really take care of yourself? Are you your own best advocate and cheerleader?

To start with, can you say "Good morning" to yourself? I started doing this fifteen years ago, when I leased my first office space. I'd unlock the door, say "Good morning" to myself, aloud, and listen to the vicious answers that came from my own head: *Oh, great, James—now you sound schizophrenic. You're finally losing it.*

The next day, I'd say it again. More nasty voices: *Wow—egotistical much?* But I kept at it. And at some point, it became much more of a friendly, two-way conversation.

Good morning, James. How are you today?

You know, I'm a little tired, but I love this office, and that babbling brook sounds as perfect as the day I first plugged it in.

You have my permission to feel ridiculous while saying good morning to yourself. Give it a try.

Self-identity is your concept of your value and significance in relation to the rest of the world. It's how you present yourself, how you measure yourself against who you ideally want to be, and how you filter out the performance reviews that stream in from the outside. A strong self-identity helps you advocate for yourself, explain yourself, redeem yourself.

Ideally, you develop a strong self-identity out of the unconditional positive regard of those around you, from people believing in you beyond the shadow of a doubt. But if, again, your world has been less than ideal, there are still ways to shore up and strengthen the pillar of self-identity, to embed that positive regard within yourself.

Both Pillars, Together

We need a firm foundation—resting on both pillars—if the most important qualities are to take root inside us and flourish. These qualities include, but are not limited to:

- Courage
- Confidence
- Persistence
- Resilience
- The ability to take a risk
- Finding your voice
- Speaking your truth
- Giving voice to your ideas
- Repairing the world

- Apologizing and making amends…and

- Reaching your potential—though you may have given up thinking that was possible.

I'm here to tell you it *is* possible, and I speak from experience. Take a moment to contemplate how reaching your potential might feel—or how empowering it would be to possess just a few of the qualities listed above. What if you just…could?

It seems as if some people are born with the two pillars firmly in place, raised in safe, loving households. Others capitalized on favorable conditions—or developed the right skills—to build their own pillars and keep them in good repair.

Unfortunately, none of that is typical for people with ADHD. If you're seen as someone who comes up with wild ideas but never follows through, or if you see yourself that way—never mind, for now, whether there's any truth to either perception—your pillars are going to be shaky foundations indeed.

You probably know how that feels—to be rooting around, scrambling to make sense of the most recent back-against-the-wall scenario, wondering where you put your courage and confidence. Sometimes you're able to assemble a big stack of ideas on how to get through this next life event, and sometimes you can sort of climb up on top of the stack, high enough to get some kind of perspective. But you're never quite sure how you got there, and then something—seemingly from out of nowhere—comes along and knocks you off again.

If your self-esteem and self-identity are balanced on an unstable foundation and you're called upon to act confidently or courageously, it can throw you into a tailspin. How can you stand firmly on a pile of rubble?

You can't. But you can dig in and start rebuilding.

IMPORTANT TOOLS

We thrive, as opposed to survive, when we learn to know ourselves. Sounds good, right? As a matter of fact, though, it can be kind of scary, because as we begin to see ourselves on a deep level, we can't help but uncover signs of the damage and pain caused by the Emotional Distress Syndrome. But we're also likely to find evidence of the unconditional love we have for ourselves, even if it's deeply buried. Thriving means being able to hold the tension between these two revelations—the pain and the love—and just be there for yourself, even if you think no one else is. The outside world may not notice when this happens to you, but the change is quite noticeable on the inside.

The concepts and tools I'm about to introduce to you are meant to strengthen that sense of loving and supporting yourself. It's going to take some work, but the work is pretty concrete.

If you can do that, you can reset yourself whenever you hit a roadblock, a setback, or anything that restarts your brain in Panic Mode.

If you can take on the ongoing, rewarding task of rebuilding yourself, you can hone the undervalued skill of knowing when you need outside help, asking for it, and even getting it!

Knowing yourself can bring a kind of alertness you may not have experienced much, especially with the ADHD fog of distraction clouding your brain. This clarity can be startling, but incredibly useful. When you get thrown off course—and you will, of course—you can use that clarity to focus on the strong connection you've made with yourself.

And believe it or not, there will come a time when you become accustomed to addressing yourself with love and self-knowledge. This can be deeply transformative. It can also provide you with much-needed moments of simpleminded goofiness; you might be surprised at how much laughter emanates from the TLEC office. We also offer a complete menu of crying, sulking, complaining, arguing and railing at the gods, but laughter is the only constant.

But back to our more conventional methods.

With the exception of Eye Movement Desensitization and Reprocessing (EMDR), you don't need a trained clinician to teach you to use the tools I'm about to describe. You don't need an advanced degree to operate them or play around with them. Some you probably already own, even if they've been rattling around in the back of your brain, unused.

And some of them—mindfulness, for instance—are very much in the current vocabulary. You get the sense that they "work" for anyone who takes the time to use them. Others—such as cultivating a healthy imagination—may have a particular resonance for people with ADHD, while more linear thinkers may find them frustrating.

In any case, my aim is to familiarize you with these tools and concepts. So get comfortable. Think of the list that follows as a smorgasbord for your brain, and allow yourself to be choosy. Read through, keep an open mind, and take note of the subjects that appeal to you, as well as anything that brings out your inner skeptic, or even freaks you out a little. No rules, just tools. We'll talk about when and how to use them later.

The Tool of Acceptance

Acceptance gives you the courage to face your ADHD.

- Accept—that this is how your brain is set up.
- Accept—that your brain chemistry is the way it is. Don't label it as something that's wrong with you, bad, or broken.

- Accept—the responsibility to understand and educate yourself. It won't be easy, but it could be interesting.
- Accept—that you'll always have to bring your brain back into balance.
- Accept—the wisdom and IQ you carry, in spite of, or even because of, your ADHD.
- Accept—that ADHD is not the main feature of your identity. It's just something about you, far from the only thing about you.
- Accept—the possibility of treatment. From now on, you'll be the most important member of your treatment team.
- Accept—that your life will continue to have its ups and downs, as it always has. There may even be some poetry in your lifelong quest for equilibrium. Of course, I'm not the first person to think of that, or to write about it.
- Accept—yourself. Notice I didn't say "Love yourself" or "Try not to hate yourself" or "Repeat positive affirmations to yourself, about yourself." Never mind all that. Just, right now, for this moment, accept yourself.

My grandmother kept Kahlil Gibran's *The Prophet* on her nightstand. Here's what he had to say on the subject of balancing passion and reason:

> *"Your reason and your passion are the rudder and the sails of your seafaring soul. If either your sails or your rudder be broken, you can but toss and drift, or else be held at a standstill in mid-seas.*
>
> *For reason, ruling alone, is a force confining; and passion, unattended, is a flame that burns to its own destruction. Therefore let your soul exalt your reason to the height of passion, that it may sing; And let it direct your passion with reason, that your passion may live through its own daily resurrection, and like the phoenix rise above its own ashes."*

The Tool of Mindfulness

Mindfulness practice acts as a pause button, and I've never met anyone who didn't need to pause once in a while. The ritual of letting distractions fall away by concentrating on the present moment has been practiced for millennia, in cultures all over the world. Meditation isn't even exclusive to humans—lots of different mammals have been observed taking mental breaks, resting and gazing, looking at the world without reacting to it.

Meditation, they say, is the simplest path to enlightenment.

It's also beautifully complex, although the scientific community is beginning to untangle its mysteries. FMRI images of stressed-out brains, before and after mindfulness practice, seem to indicate that the brain can actually repair frayed neural connections. It's amazing, but not inaccurate, to consider that a small amount of conscious breathing, practiced daily, can spur the brain to repair itself.

For those of us with ADHD, the implications are very encouraging. Think about it: We have more trouble than most people, not only in concentrating, but in deciding what's worth concentrating on and what can wait. Mindfulness helps us sort it out. At its most basic, meditation is simply deciding to *pay attention to what is happening now, without judging the experience.*

Your breath, for instance. Sitting comfortably, noticing your breathing. When your mind wanders away, you gently bring it back to your breath. Doing this over and over again is the only training some of us ever get in just paying attention. If you lead a life of epic distraction, followed by epic recriminations when you forget something important, imagine how restorative it feels to just *be*—to bring yourself back when you wander off, but without any of the usual negative messages.

In general, people with ADHD need a deliberate framework with which to begin a mindfulness practice, and, as with exercise, it's important to realize that some days will be better than others.

TRY THIS AT HOME

MEDITATION

Remember: *Everyone gets distracted, all the time.* After you notice you're distracted, gently guide yourself back to whatever you decided to focus on—your breath, a sound or a sacred word, for instance.

Any amount of meditation, even a couple of minutes, is better than waiting until an uninterrupted half-hour opens up in your schedule. Twenty minutes is said to be ideal, but again, two or three minutes can be very powerful.

Check out the vast selection of meditation smartphone apps, in which someone—usually someone with a calm, non-American accent—talks you through six or seven minutes of guided relaxation. You'll be relieved to hear that there's a never-ending selection to choose from. If you get bored with one app, try a different one.

Ready to move on from guided meditation? Set a timer to ring in five or ten minutes. Sit in silence. When the timer rings, use it as a reminder of whatever you intended to focus on.

Need a break from sitting? Try a meditative walk, somewhere you can move slowly and deliberately, concentrating on your breath.

You can apply the walking-meditation concept while listening to a piece of music or washing a dish. Or try inserting contemplative mini-breaks into your daily activities.

Inner chatter has a tendency to boil up during meditation. When it does, give it a neutral, non-judgmental label, such as "worrying," "planning" or "thinking," and go back to your breath.

Instead of this:

What the hell is wrong with me? I was supposed to be concentrating on my breath, but I've been replaying that argument with my girlfriend and wondering why she posted that thing on Instagram. I'm an idiot! I'll never figure this out! Plus, why wasn't I invited to that party? Probably because everyone hates me.

Try something like this:

Does everyone hate me? Oh, that's a thought. Back to the breath. Breathe. In. Out. In. Out. Instagram…Oh, that's thinking. Back to the breath. Breathe. Oh, the sound of a bird. Sound. Breathe. Breathe.

See what I mean about the pause button? Intuitively, it makes sense that we ADHD-ers need frequent time-outs. It also makes scientific sense. A recent research study of Finnish teenagers showed mindfulness practice to be as effective as ADHD medication in strengthening cognitive control, also known as the ability to focus.

My clients may not always feel like beginning to meditate, but they are all always happy to have done so.

"I didn't know what being gentle with myself felt like AT ALL until Guy described it during my first meditation. I had been told many times to be gentle with myself or not to be so hard on myself or to stop stressing, but until I could intuitively "feel" it, I was unable to do it myself. I didn't know what gentle was. I just knew what I was "doing wrong." It has helped incredibly! I can honestly say I don't get worked up about much anymore. It's gotten easy to be curious and observe and then keep a good, relaxed perspective."

I do have clients who report feeling antsy or restless during group mindfulness exercises, but I tell them it's always okay to just stop meditating and read a book or go get some water. That's the point: You *practice* meditation, but there's nothing to achieve, and no gold stars are handed out for the quietest, most focused person in the group.

So this is my recommendation: start meditating and see where it takes you. One-minute, three-minute or five-minute sessions are great places to start, though if you want to hit the pause button for longer, you should certainly go ahead.

The Tool of Spirituality

I'm not a preacher or a minister or a spiritual guru, but I don't think there's any shortcut around the issue of spirituality. In my opinion, everyone needs it at some level. I believe that without a spiritual connection, all therapeutic techniques devolve into gimmicks. I believe everyone's capable of spirituality, including agnostics and atheists.

All this "I believe!" makes some of my clients uncomfortable!

I get it, but bear with me.

First of all, what do I mean by *spirituality?*

Spirituality is whatever calms the ultimate anxiety of our existence—the fact that we don't know what happens before we're born or after we die. And that *is* the big anxiety, isn't it? As humans, this is the one question we don't have an answer for. Most humans feel some anxiety about this uneasy state of affairs, so imagine how it affects those of us with ADHD, who walk hand in hand with anxiety.

As you know, our distractibility and hyperfocus can overwhelm our brains into a near-constant startled state that makes it very difficult for us to unplug and calm down. Spirituality shows us the way out of that trap, because spiritual experiences have the power to neutralize primal threats.

Let's go back to the science. What calms the threat response—the fight, flight or freeze? That which is known. So when our cavewoman ancestor, the one being chased by a saber-toothed tiger, managed to climb a sturdy tree, familiar information flooded her brain. *I'm in a tall tree. The beast can't climb this tree. I am safe.* That's pretty basic, but there's more to it. Beyond basic safety, her brain registered a feeling of connectedness to something outside herself. Maybe she was grateful to the tree itself. Maybe she felt lucky to have been "given" this vertical escape route. Maybe she felt smart for having discovered the right tree at the right time, or strong for having the ability to haul herself up into it. Or maybe she felt a renewed sense of connection to all the other humans with whom she now got to spend another day of life. In my opinion, all these feelings are expressions of spirituality, and all of them have a quantifiable calming effect on the brain.

Most spiritual experiences are grounded in the present. In other words, there's an element of mindfulness to spirituality. But mindfulness and spirituality are two different things. Mindfulness is detached—a clear-headed observation of what is or isn't happening in the moment. Spirituality takes that observation and adds a relationship: an interconnectedness, if not to other human beings (or all human beings), then to the universe, or a force for good, or just the sense that being alive makes sense. Humans need connection; think of how instinctively infants crave skin-to-skin contact.

The point is this: Spirituality, however you want to construct it for yourself, is the most effective weapon against existential anxiety.

Notice I haven't mentioned God, organized religion or any particular belief system—all that is up to you. I've worked with religiously devout people, atheists and everything in between, and they've all managed to come up with a construct that works for them. People who have no traditional sense of God may find a sense of grounding in the earth itself. You may find it when you put on your favorite boots, or glance up at the works of original art hanging on your walls. I have even heard tell (I won't say by whom) of a Higher Power who manifests as a friendly polar bear.

For me personally, spirituality is whatever adds meaning to my daily life—and that usually means something I can see. I've covered my workplace with objects of meaning, from living plants to original artwork to quotes and sayings in frames, and lately, I've been adding big, polished rocks. I find they serve as touchstones.

Your own brand of spirituality might involve closing your eyes for a moment and focusing on your breath. Or it might be down-to-earth and action-centered. I have a client who helps out at a local church serving breakfast tacos to homeless people as a way of expressing the belief that all human beings are in some way responsible for each other.

Another client constructed a small labyrinth in her backyard for walking meditation and prayer. Others are members of churches, synagogues, ashrams, mosques and meditation groups.

The Tool of EMDR
(Eye Movement Desensitization and Reprocessing)
Many of the tools and techniques I use at The Life Empowerment Center could fall under the heading of Do-It-Yourself. EMDR is an exception.

To experience its benefits, you really do need to find a certified EMDR therapist. Luckily, this is easy to do, and, depending on the issues you bring to therapy, you can make a lot of progress in a relatively short time. I wouldn't recommend it if I didn't believe it was almost indispensable in helping my clients strengthen their self-esteem and self-identity and to desensitize high states of distress.

EMDR Therapy, developed by Francine Shapiro, Ph.D., was originally designed to help heal instances of trauma—anything from physical assault to recurring, disturbing memories and PTSD. While experimenting with ways to recruit both hemispheres of the brain, Dr. Shapiro directed her subjects to move their eyes back and forth. She discovered that these "eye movements" brought on a calm, relaxed state of mind. Even while mentally relieving traumatic events, her subjects became less anxious, allowing them to revisit or re-process the event from a "safe" perspective. Having processed disturbing memories or traumas, clients often learn how to use EMDR techniques to make positive changes in their lives, calm daily stress and solve problems. In other words, they move from "symptom reduction" into "comprehensive treatment."

EMDR has been researched exhaustively. The American Psychiatric Association, the Department of Veterans Affairs, the Department of Defense and the World Health Organization all list EMDR as a "strongly recommended" treatment. For more information, go to the source: the EMDR Institute, at emdr.com.

I discovered EMDR in the early Nineties, became certified by the EMDR Institute in 1994, and have found this therapy to be indispensable ever since.

Here's an example: Renee, a 46-year-old client with ADHD, had participated in one of my long-term therapy groups and done well. She reconnected with me for counseling when her state agency job ended and she found herself at a career crossroads. Her passion had always been theater, and she now had time to attend an acting class, but felt too paralyzed by fear to actually show up in person. Though she realized all actors deal with some fear and stress, she imagined that her own was so severe because of her ADHD that she could never be a *real* actor. In session, I asked her to name her three greatest fears about attending the class. Not surprisingly, ADHD played into all three—memorizing lines (distractibility), being on time (skewed time orientation) and stage fright (getting trapped in the stress of the moment). Using the EMDR "tappers" (hand-held vibrating devices that alternate stimuli between the left and right hands), Renee was able to slow down her breathing, focus on each individual stressor, and use her imagination (and some direction from me) to reframe each scene in far more positive and interesting ways. Through EMDR, she was able to visit and revisit her fears until her anxiety died almost completely away. She attended, finished and enjoyed her acting class.

During the first few sessions with a new client, I almost always introduce EMDR. Clients I see regularly will request it whenever they need it. Clients I haven't seen in years will sometimes come by for a one-session EMDR "tune-up." It can be used in conjunction with all the other tools I hope to give you in this book. In short, I'm sorry I can't teach you to do it yourself, but certified clinicians are now widely available.

The Tool of Imagination

Imagination is one of the highest and best uses of the mind, and, in my experience, one of the most therapeutic. Connecting to your imagination is the best way to rebuild that internal sense of safety that may have been missing for years, or perhaps was never there at all.

And yet, when I teach this skill—because, odd as it sounds, you can *learn* this stuff—I've gotten the reaction that it feels hokey or weird. So let me just confirm: You can repair your neural networks using weird, hokey techniques that may strike you as strange or even silly. There's science behind the mind's ability to dream, daydream, envision and re-make reality. Research has shown that when we imagine a scene or event in great detail, our brains respond as if it were really happening.

You may have noticed that our society doesn't always reward big, colorful imaginations, which is too bad. But consider this: What you do with your imagination may not be any of society's business. By definition, your imagination belongs to you. Because, after all, who "dreamed it up"? Think about it: Whatever you construct in your imagination gets built in the blink of an eye! Walt Disney said, "The first rule of imagination is there are no rules." Exactly. If you have ADHD, that probably requires no explanation.

Your imagination is your very own internal video editing tool. You can use it to go backward or forward in time, to change or expand on actual events, or construct a new reality out of spare parts salvaged from the old. Feel free to mess around with the sound and the picture—as well as the smell, touch and taste. Seen through the lens of a healthy imagination, your life can seem a lot less like a mess and a lot more like an adventure. Most important, developing your imagination strengthens your relationship with yourself. That's what I want for my clients as a base for all the work that follows.

A lot of my ADHD clients interact very naturally with their imaginations. As soon as I raise the subject, they go to town, as if their imaginations were destinations, even dream vacations. Finally—a place where they can do whatever they want, without having to justify or explain it to anyone! That freedom appears to be the ultimate safety net, the feeling that no one can question our internal strength, because we know it's there, having "seen" it.

Other clients, on the other hand, do *not* go to town. They may be more linear thinkers, or they may have had it drummed into them that hanging around in their imagination is a waste of time. If I tell this kind of client, "Okay, close your eyes, go inside … ," I may get a wary look.

In that case, I lead them gently back into childhood, a time when most of us had easy relationships with our imaginations—talking freely with imaginary friends or stuffed animals, or spending hours, alone or with other kids, pretending to be whatever we wanted to be. I encourage clients to tune into those memories, and then to zero in on whichever of their six senses feels strongest. (As a child, could you "hear" applause? A marching band? "See" a glacier on a hot day? "Touch" the soft coat of a dog that died years ago?)

If they devote just a few minutes each day to making contact with their imaginations, the awkwardness melts away. And once the childlike sense of imagination has been rekindled, a lot of us remember that our imagination once served as a refuge from the continual stress of being alive. Taking that refuge doesn't make you escapist or irresponsible; in fact, combined with some of the other tools, it can be very, very therapeutic.

Be open to what your imagination has to offer.

The Tool of Intuition

A dictionary will tell you something like this:

> **Intuition:** *a natural ability or power that makes it possible to know something without any proof or evidence; a feeling that guides a person to act a certain way without fully understanding why.*

"Don't try to comprehend with your mind," Madeleine L'Engle wrote in the great YA novel *A Wrinkle in Time.* "Your minds are very limited. Use your intuition."

Albert Einstein, a scientist who respected intuition, took it a step further: "The intuitive mind is a sacred gift and the rational mind is a faithful servant. We have created a society that honors the servant and has forgotten the gift."

Einstein knew what he was talking about. All of us received the gift of intuition at birth, but few of us use it. And most people with ADHD, based on life-long misunderstandings of who they are and how they operate, don't trust their own internal experience. Any help they get teaches them to rely on strategies that come at them from the outside: things like research-based protocols and medication. They're rarely taught how to trust the intuition they have, or how to develop the intuition they don't have (yet).

Intuition is your sixth sense, your gut reaction. Intuition is infused knowledge, or *knowing without knowledge.*

People with ADHD don't necessarily have a stronger sense of intuition, but they may be able to use it more effectively than their "normal" friends. This may be the upside of the under-active prefrontal cortex. (And you thought it was all bad news.) The ADHD mind has trouble settling down in the details, but from its vantage point, floating around above the ground, it can sometimes perceive intricate patterns and trends.

What's your experience with intuition? How does it show up for you personally? Do you hear, see or feel things? Do you have sensations that are indescribable to others? Just to give you an example, my own intuition feels like a kind of pull, as if a small child were taking my hand and leading me somewhere. My curiosity and observation kick in and I begin to see synergies and connections, rhymes, reasons, even miracles.

But, wait—how can we trust intuition? How do we tell the difference between intuition and impulsivity, the ADHD adult's go-to decision-making tool? After all, both intuition and impulsivity could be described as *aha* moments: *I know! I'll do this!* But where intuition sounds as if it leads somewhere wise and grounded, impulsivity has gotten most of us into trouble.

Here's a cheat sheet to help you tell the difference.

Impulsive thought: Look at that shiny thing! I want that thing *now!*

Intuitive thought: If I can block out all the shiny distractions and slow down a little, I can perceive an interesting, glimmery possibility, and something about it just feels right. I don't have to do anything about it right now, but I'm looking forward to finding out more about it soon.

Impulsive thought: I think I'm in trouble. Hey! Maybe Person X can save my life/get me out of trouble/bail me out of jail! Will they mind if I call them at 2 a.m.? Nah! I'm gonna go for it!

Intuitive thought: I think I'm worried about something. It's kind of funny that I think Person X can magically take away this distressing unpleasant emotion at 2 a.m. He might not think it was all that amusing, though. So, forgetting about all this Big, World-Ending Trouble, is there one small step I could take now? Does it feel right, in a quiet way?

I think you get the idea.

Listening to that "still, small voice" is an underrated skill. I've actually taken classes in intuition. But I notice that some people with ADHD resist the whole concept, mostly because of fears that may sound familiar. After all, if you start acting on "gut instincts," you might fail, perhaps spectacularly. The other shoe might drop!

Yes, it might. But learn to recognize and cultivate your intuition in spite of the possibility of failure. Because, as the voice of your true self, intuition is very useful in counteracting distracting or destructive impulsivity.

So how to strengthen intuition without fueling impulsivity? Practice your gut instinct on little things. *What kind of drink do I want, what kind of food?* When nothing earth-shaking is at stake, tune into the art of the snap decision. Once in a while, plan a date night—with your significant other, or just alone—without any particular plan and just your intuition as guide. See where it leads you. You might end up in a wonderful place.

The next time you're struggling with an issue or a challenge, ask yourself, "What is the next and simplest action I could take with the information I have?" See what comes to you—within a few seconds, no longer. See if you get a "good" impulse, an idea or suggestion that comes from your wise sixth sense rather than the confusion of ADHD.

Don't overthink it. If it doesn't "work," try it again another time. There are many ways to hone your intuition skills, but none that you need to leap into right now. Just be open to the idea that they exist.

> ## TRY THIS AT HOME
> ### INTUITION WALK
> Find a time when you have no set schedule—a couple of hours, or a whole day. Go outside and take a walk. When you get to a corner, ask yourself: *Which way should I turn? What's my intuition on this?* Follow that *immediate* response. See where it takes you.
>
> When and if you get tired of walking, do something else. Ask your intuition what that something else might be. Go for it. Whenever you reach a crossroads, ask for guidance again. And again, see where it takes you.
>
> Feel the freedom that comes with this type of decision-making. It might look impulsive to a casual observer, but it isn't, because you're not reacting to a threat. The sense of danger has been replaced by grounded curiosity.

The Tool of Humor

I doubt the wisdom of going into a detailed, academic description of what humor is and why it's therapeutic. But I'll say this: I've had to rehabilitate my ability to laugh about life. Early in my career, while working at a psychiatric hospital, I attended a lecture on humor, given by a brilliantly funny minister. He reminded us that every time we laugh, we're deep-breathing, and we're also making it possible, just for a moment, not to think about anything but *what's so funny*. Both are very helpful for our overactive minds.

To embrace humor, you must risk looking stupid. I recommend looking stupid as an exercise in humility and joy. It's never too late to learn how. Your (God-given?) ability to look silly and embrace humor may have been stymied, as mine was, by years spent using humor as a bludgeon—as a way to make fun of others, or myself. But all that was pretty easy to overcome by simply taking a deep breath and forgetting to take myself so seriously. A few of my clients have even taken improv comedy classes, where they learned the proper way to recover after messing up on stage, or in life: Take a grand, theatrical circus bow! Do this immediately! Then wait for the applause.

And now, a word from Mel Brooks:

"If you're alive, you've got to flap your arms and legs, you've got to jump around a lot, for life is the very opposite of death, and therefore you must at very least think noisy and colorfully, or you're not alive."

The Tool of Strategic, Therapeutic Daydreaming

You may have been told that daydreaming is pointless. You may have been told to cut it out, especially if you've had trouble keeping your mind on the task at hand. Okay, but let me just say that when you're trying to rebuild your self, daydreaming *is* the task at hand. All the previous tools can be combined into this one.

And another thing: If you have ADHD, you're probably a pretty skilled daydreamer. Good for you. You're going to enjoy this next part.

YOUR EMOTIONAL SAFE PLACE

My what?

Your Emotional Safe Place.

My Emotional Safe Place?

Yes, your Emotional Safe Place. Inside your imagination, your psyche, your shared consciousness, or whatever you feel comfortable calling it, there is such a place. It will need some cleaning and airing out, and definitely some major imaginative touches, but it's there.

How will you know it when you "see" it? And what is "it," anyway? I'm glad you asked.

Your Emotional Safe Place (ESP, unrelated to extrasensory perception) is a personalized, private mental refuge—perhaps the most strategic, therapeutic daydream of them all. You are its architect; you create it in your mind's eye. It's a place where time stands still, where you feel safe, comfortable, protected and free to be alive.

If you seek peace, it's the most peaceful place imaginable.

If you crave stimulation, your Emotional Safe Place is exciting, and then some.

Either way, it's 100 percent safe and 100 percent private. You don't have to earn it or deserve it or work for it or surrender it to the authorities. It belongs to you and you alone. It's unconditional. It is what it is and it isn't what it isn't. You will go there whenever you need a break, a strategy or a vacation. When you're out of ideas, you'll go to your Emotional Safe Place to regroup.

What are we waiting for? Let's go.

TRY THIS AT HOME

A VISIT TO YOUR EMOTIONAL SAFE PLACE

- Find a little spare time—10 to 20 minutes.
- Stop what you're doing. Begin to slow your thoughts.
- Get into a comfortable position, probably sitting, but possibly lying down. Uncross your legs. Sense your body, wherever it is. Start to observe rather than to react. Close your eyes. Focus on your breathing. Feel the relaxed rhythm of your breathing (for ten to twenty breaths). Imagine experiencing a sense of peace.
- Notice that. Now begin to see an island—an island in your sea of consciousness, an island, or any other geographic feature, created by you, for you. A place you want to be. A place you're drawn to. Think about positive experiences you've had, in places where you felt peaceful or serene. Remember times when all your cares slipped away. If you want to be there again, go there now.
- Use the senses that most appeal to you—your sense of smell, sight, hearing, touch, taste. Tap into your senses to find what you need to nurture your soul. The more you use your senses, the stronger the neural net becomes.
- There are no limitations—everything is possible to have, and if something doesn't feel right, it disappears. This is not a place for judgment, criticism or harm. These concepts simply do not exist in your emotional safe place.
- Feel your connection to this place. Walk down any path that appeals to you. How do these surroundings make you feel? Relaxed? Happy? Nurtured? Adventurous? Whatever you want

more of, experience more of. This is your place. Visit whenever you want.

- It doesn't have to be an island. Maybe it's a galaxy far, far away. Maybe it's a tiny, magical closet or a fairy garden or a speeding train headed to parts unknown.
- Open doors, pick flowers, turn up the music, jump into the lake. Or the bull ring, or the stratosphere.
- Or don't. Do whatever you want and nothing you don't.
- Stay a while. As long as you like.
- (Five minutes pass.)
- Remember what this place is called—your Emotional Safe Place. You can return whenever you like.
- Stay as long as you like. Then open your eyes.
- Welcome back. How was that?

Your Emotional Safe Place is the jumping-off point for a lot of the positive, adventurous work you're about to do. If you've spent a lifetime on edge, waiting nervously for your next screw-up, you need a really strong ESP to counteract all that vigilance.

You can go to your Emotional Safe Place whenever you like, and the more often you go there, the greater detail you'll be able to see in your mind's eye, and the more strength you'll bring to your pillar of self-esteem.

In your Emotional Safe Place, there truly are no conditions. So what you need and want, you get. Most people thrive on unconditional acceptance and regard. How can this not be good?

Having had an Emotional Safe Place of my own for many years, I feel confident suggesting ways you can use yours, and please feel free to add your own. Go to your Emotional Safe Place when you:

- Want an emotional sense of well-being and calm
- Need to lull yourself back to sleep
- Are emotionally distressed and long to feel safe
- Need to reset your focus and concentration
- Feel generally crazy
- Feel yourself spinning into reactivity
- Need to be somewhere you're not
- Need a boost or a bump or a break, or just a time-out
- Crave escape from a threat or reality or everyday boredom or spiritual malaise

While you're at it, go for no reason at all.

The more often you go to your ESP, the more specifically you'll "see" its many attractions, the more therapeutic your visits will be, and the more precisely your imaginary place will be calibrated to your real-life needs. I'm reminded of a client who needed comfort and grounding. As general contractor of his Emotional Safe Place, he installed a deep pool of cool water that was magically protective. Floating in that water infused him with all the comfort and strength he needed to get connected with life in the noisy, complex world. He was able to use this very cool pool in all sorts of stressful work situations—before a sure-to-be tense meeting or conference call, for instance. He even summarized the concept of the pool in one secret word (he never told me what it was) and would often write that word on a pad during a stressful situation.

Not sure how to start building your own ESP? Well, where and when do you last remember feeling calm yet interested, connected, at peace?

Tune in to those memories. Now consider your six senses. Smell an antique rose, or bacon frying. Taste a mango. Feel rain on your face. Hear your favorite bedtime story being read aloud, to you alone, by a favorite relative or some brilliant Shakespearean actor. What do you want to see, hear, touch, taste, smell and feel in your private refuge?

The more specific you can be in furnishing your ESP, the more you'll strengthen your neural networks.

I constructed my own Emotional Safe Place nearly thirty years ago, and I'd love to show you around. There's the cloud room, where I go to float in the clouds. There's the wardrobe room, where I can change into different outfits and become different characters. I've remodeled the living room quite a bit over the years. Right now it has a 180-degree panoramic window, and the house rotates so I can see the beach or the mountains or the rainforest or my acre of crepe myrtles in full bloom. (Naturally, they're always in full bloom.)

And this is only the beginning. I could also show you the large ring of 100-foot pine trees, with a perfect fire burning right in the center and a full moon in the night sky. It's 42 degrees. Owls hoot in the trees.

You could check out the perfect 82-degree aqua water that laps at my feet as I sit on my private beach, luxuriating in the offshore breeze that always blows between seven and eight miles per hour, because that's how I like to experience the salt air of the ocean.

That hundred-foot waterfall? I installed it during a Colorado vacation, while sitting in front of the real thing. It took about 20 minutes: I meditated, watched the waterfall, and went back and forth between opening and closing my eyes until every detail was perfect.

And don't even get me started on the 45-foot long purple dragon I ride around on whenever I get the chance! Her name is Emperor, and she and I think exactly alike.

So welcome to the vast empire in my head, and now, please leave and go create your own. Not only will you find this construction job to be satisfying, creative, relaxing and downright fun, but you'll be glad to have your ESP as a retreat when the next emotional tsunami hits.

If all this sounds a bit childish, I'm fine with that. In fact, I got a lot of my best ideas while working with children, who don't really need to be taught how to build imaginary worlds and often have plenty to teach us adults.

Back when I first came up with the ESP concept, I was helping an eight-year-old develop one of his own. He loved animals, so he put all kinds in his ESP. Then the thought occurred to him that the lions might feast on the zebras, as they do in the real animal kingdom. I wondered aloud how he might handle this situation in his ESP. He got a very bright look on his face and declared that he had a solution: He'd put fake zebras in his ESP, to attract the lions. When a lion bit a fake zebra, a trap door would open, releasing an endless supply of fresh meat. Result: The lions would never hurt the real zebras.

It's an excellent example of the ESP loophole: You're allowed to make impossible things possible. In my own ESP, for instance, I'll often snack on mangoes, but because I find them tedious to peel, the mangoes that fall from the tree in my ESP have been bred to have a banana-like skin. I had fun inventing the Miraculous Easy-Eat Mango. I like knowing I can solve small problems with my imagination. It doesn't matter that it takes longer to peel real mangoes in my real kitchen in my real life.

"I put a Tinkerbell-like fairy in my ESP. She zips around in her little cartoon outfit putting away all the paperwork, paying the bills, washing the dishes, just creating order out of chaos. I don't have to leave her a list or help her figure out what order to do things in—in fact, she wants me out of her way, not bugging her. She'd rather I don't even talk to her. We have nothing in common, and she's really busy. But when I feel overwhelmed by niggling tasks and I can't figure out how long they're going to take—or frankly, if I'll ever finish them, or even start them—I take a quick vacation at my ESP and watch my little Task Fairy zap her magic wand at all the things that bug me. Zap! Zap! Zap! It's very restorative.

I still have all my chores to do when I return from my ESP, but somehow the Task Fairy takes a lot of their scary power away. Somehow I feel much better about my ability to do what has to be done—or choose not to."

Goofing around in your Emotional Safe Place is good for your emotional well-being. That's my professional opinion, based on years of professional observation. Here are a few more glimpses inside ESPs:

"Yes, I have an Emotional Safe Place. In a way, I have always had it with me, but didn't realize I could access it on command. I stumbled upon it by accident a few times, and now I come back whenever I want to. I find it helps to go there just before I tackle something formidable, as well as afterwards, to celebrate. In it, I'm always wearing my favorite jeans."

"I find it a helpful exercise. Part of keeping it safe is not sharing too much about it, but in my case, it's its own planet, complete with moons."

"Yes, it's a place from my past, at the ranch, where I would go when things got too tough. While working with James, I added a stream or brook and all the safe wildlife of my youth. I still go to this safe place when I am stressed—I feel my now-deceased family all around me, looking out for me, waiting to carry me home when the time comes. There are no words to describe the peace I feel from this experience."

"ADHD can be mentally exhausting. My Emotional Safe Place allows me to escape somewhere to regroup and cope with stressors. I've constructed a non-judgmental place in my mind where I feel safe, loved, supported, protected, strong, calm, secure and relaxed...the total opposite of the chaotic feelings I usually have jumbled in my brain."

"At the heart of my ESP is a tree with an interior stairway and doors at various levels. One door leads to an eternal campfire which I share with old friends and former selves. Another leads to the cockpit of my father's 42' Hinkley sloop."

"My ESP is my safe haven! It's a Willy-Wonka-esque paradise, a mix of imaginative fantasies I had as a child and my current vision of joy and comfort. Initially I would visit only during my meditation time; I found my brain was able to grasp the ESP easier than the traditional "count your breath/focus on your breath" technique. However, I found the more I went to my ESP, the more centered and grounded I felt. So now I keep it running in the back of my mind. If I need to take a break, I'm there. All of my past pets who have died are there. Being able to reconnect with them gives me so much healing, peace, serenity and joy."

I love reading those descriptions—the genius of all those TLEC emotional architects! It's almost childlike, but then, nothing compares to an actual child when it comes to the imagination.

You can capture your Emotional Safe Place experiences and visuals by writing about them, speaking them into a digital voice recorder, sketching, doodling, singing—it's up to you. You might create a collage of pictures to remind you of your ESP and keep it on your desk at work, or nearby at home to help nurture the ESP habit. Or surround yourself with tangible objects that represent your ESP or somehow evoke its feeling of particular calm and safety. Or don't do any of the above! If you don't feel like it, no problem, because your Emotional Safe Place, by its very definition, will always be there for you.

Remember, your ESP is meant to be private—a healthy, or "functional," secret. This privacy constitutes the "safe" part of your Emotional Safe Place. Be selective about whom you share it with—ideally, only those you're sure will be unconditionally positive and encouraging. In fact, I encourage my clients to create a secret passageway to their ESP. It could be a number combination, an invisible force field activated by your DNA, a hidden laundry chute—whatever works for you. Once you know your ESP is completely secure, you can truly relax into the process.

I recently added a high-tech DNA-recognition system to my own ESP, along with my patented smile security software layer. (I have to smile to get in. My smile, of course, is unique.) While I was tinkering, I installed an outdoor fireplace. But that's just me. You get to outfit your ESP any way you want.

YOUR MENTAL SUPPORT GROUP

With your Emotional Safe Place firmly set in your imagination, I now encourage you to add a Mental Support Group (MSG)—a support group, chosen by you, whose wisdom and humor and just-right-ness you can access whenever you want. Wouldn't it be great to have an advisory board on call, a board whose only agenda was seeing that you get to live your life to the fullest? They'd always be happy to hear from you. They'd welcome your midnight brainstorms and your surly six a.m. stuck-in-traffic venting. Plus, they'd think of solutions that would never occur to you.

A nice scenario, I think we can all agree. But how on earth do people like us, who have trouble organizing our own lives, put together a group like this?

Cleary, this task is tailor-made for strategic, therapeutic daydreaming. And, while you may have to cover your bathroom mirror with sticky notes just to remind yourself to brush and floss, you have this daydreaming thing figured out. So let's get to it.

TRY THIS AT HOME
RECRUITING A MENTAL SUPPORT GROUP

Stop the carnival. Find some spare time—ten to twenty minutes. Get into a comfortable position and reduce distractions as best you can.

- Slow down your breathing. Concentrate on that, if anything. Your breath, going in, going out.
- Go inside.
- Begin to engage your power of compassionate curiosity.

- See what is.
- Now bring your thoughts to something that might be troubling you or causing you distress. Maybe it's one of those issues, large or small, that doesn't seem to have an obvious resolution. Maybe you're between a rock and a hard place. Give this problem a name—just a few words. It doesn't matter if this is a matter of the greatest urgency or the proverbial first-world problem. Don't judge it, just name it: *Overdue tax bill. Snotty teenager. So lonely. Mid-life crisis. Sinus pain driving me nuts.*
- Imagine bringing this problem to a special group of people who have just one thing in common—concern for you. They love *you*, very specifically. They forgive you. They support you. That's what brought them together, because otherwise they might not know each other.
- This is your Mental Support Group.
- These people might be, strictly speaking, imaginary. They might be characters in a book or a movie or friends you invented before you knew how to read. They might be public figures. Anyone, real or imagined, alive or dead, can be part of your Mental Support Group, as long as you give the okay.
- Stay with this. See how these people react to the problem you put before them. Remain *compassionately curious.* Logic is great, but this is no time for logic. Just listen and observe.
- Stay as long as you want, and if it feels right, thank these people for coming when you're ready to go.

That's all there is to it. You have just created a Mental Support Group. From now on, when you find yourself in the storm of the Emotional

Distress Syndrome, you can use this group to help you triage your symptoms or formulate an emergency response. The Mental Support Group is your first intervention against emotional distress, and if you can find five minutes and a quiet corner, they can help you right away.

It usually takes a while for my clients to wrap their heads around this concept, so don't beat yourself up if you're still waiting for it to make sense. In fact, don't beat yourself up, period. There's a lot more to say about Mental Support Groups and how they help in resolving emotional distress, but before we get into that, a story.

———— Great Moments in My Imaginary History ————

Years ago, I shut the door to my office, got comfortable on the couch, and began an ongoing daydream about an emotional pit crew that could help me through any crisis. My earliest Mental Support Group was separate from my Emotional Safe Place. We met in a nice (imaginary) boardroom overlooking a mountain, with a big glass window. Larry, the psychologist I did my first ADHD work with, was there, and Lucy, my first supervisor at St. David's Hospital. And Deepak Chopra, who was just great. He'd say, "You create your own reality, James, and you're doing everything the way I'd do it, and you're really helping people." He had that slow Indian drawl.

It's hard to overstate how strongly I felt the support from everyone in the group.

Over time, two former family pets imagined their way into my MSG—our dog Luna and our rabbit Softie. They also got into my Emotional Safe Place. Here's how it happened.

I was taking a well-deserved break in my Emotional Safe Place, lying in the giant Jacuzzi I'd recently installed, and I found myself thinking that there were two things I wanted more of in my life:

1. Happiness
2. Fun

All of a sudden, Softie the rabbit bounced into the Jacuzzi room. In the blink of an eye, he became my official spokesman and archetype for happiness. It made sense, because in real life, he was always happily bouncing around. Next, Luna the dog stepped into the room. Apparently, she was the official representative from the Council on Fun. That also made sense, because the real Luna was a sheltie, always chasing balls and sticks, and the way she did it, it looked like pure, unadulterated fun.

Luna and Softie became permanent members of my MSG, which took to meeting at my Emotional Safe Place. There'd be Deepak and Lucy and Larry and Softie and Luna all gathering around the fire, inside the ring of hundred-foot pine trees. The weather was perfect—crisp and autumn-like—but if it stopped being perfect, all I had to do was "order" a change of climate.

Then George Waguespach showed up, from long ago in my past, when I was a rowdy teenager at Mount Carmel Catholic High School in Houston. One day, he had approached me and my group of rowdy friends and asked to speak to me alone. He seemed to know me—and not in the way a rebellious teen wants to be known. He looked me in the eye and said, "I just want you to know you don't have to hang with this kind of crowd. You're going to be someone really special some day. I believe in you."

At the time, I'd pretended to be embarrassed, but he'd made a strong impression. And now George was back in my corner.

Over the years, support group members have come and gone as I needed them. I've had as many as 16 people around that fire. Sometimes I'll go and listen to each person in turn. Or sometimes they'll show up without my realizing they've arrived, which is apparently what happened with Santiago, a shaman who appeared one day on top of a mountain in my ESP. Santiago doesn't do groups—I doubt I'll ever find him sitting around the fire with the rest of the gang—but that's his choice. In his own way, he's been so helpful to me.

So have my brother Ron and my mother and father—all deceased in real life, but still very alive in my MSG.

That's how it is for me. What about you? What will happen when you create a Mental Support Group? Since so much of the action takes place on an imaginary plane, can there really be any concrete benefit?

I'll tell you what happens with most of my clients. They feel overwhelming relief. Two kinds.

First, from loneliness. ADHD, as you certainly know, can be a lonely diagnosis. People ask us what's wrong, and we get all tangled up trying to craft a response that makes sense in the linear world. Or maybe no one asks us what's wrong, which sets up a different cycle of loneliness. I'm not saying we should stop trying to communicate, but it can be a tremendous relief to be able to talk things over with yourself. Your Mental Support Group is, in many ways, a sort of heightened, hyper-creative, hyper-effective version of you. All of these versions of you speak the same language. So first, there's the relief of not having to explain ourselves.

Second comes the relief of getting news we can use, sometimes after many years of searching. My clients turn to their MSGs for support, and that's what they get—a dose of confidence, a solution to a problem, a reason to feel optimistic, something to try, or something to stop trying.

"My entire life, from my earliest memories, I've always felt different. Although I've always had many friends, I've always felt misunderstood. I've dealt with depression as a repercussion of the emotional distress. But I've learned through working with James that my differences are a gift, not a hindrance. My emotional distress has lessened significantly within the last couple of years, and I believe it is due to working with James, and via his guidance, to creating an Emotional Safe Place and Mental Support Group. It's helped me to see that the behaviors I've beaten myself up for were caused by my differences in processing and not because I'm a bad person. I've been able to accept my emotional distress as a side effect of the ADHD instead of blaming myself for being an emotionally immature, socially awkward freak, as I've always seen myself. Life has opened up for me."

"I love my Mental Support Group! I love knowing that 'talking' with these incredibly supportive and wise people isn't crazy. Having the structure of the MSG and permission to use this technique is wonderful! And I realize that it's a technique to help me get in touch with my own intuition, creativity, inner guidance and even spiritual source."

"What really helped me develop the MSG was finding images online of people I wanted in it, different people for traits that I want support with—strength, courage, creativity, authenticity, compassion... Currently my MSG includes Mike Tyson, Rosa Parks, Howard Stern, Rob Zombie and Mark Houston (an AA speaker). I've had talking animals and past college professors as well."

"I was feeling completely stymied by the idea of healthy food. How am I supposed to pack a healthy lunch to take to work and have time left over to exercise? I often end up eating crap and feeling crummy about myself.

I was hoping to appoint some kind of health practitioner to my Mental Support Group—maybe a nutritionist or a famous athlete or something, but when I opened the door, my dog Rocket walked in. Obviously, he's been the expert all along. He's a cattle dog, so he's all about working and herding and paying attention. Obviously, he doesn't have ADHD. He loves routine. He loves his walks every day and his two meals, morning and night. He laid it all out for me: When it comes to healthy food, I need to think like a cattle dog. I need to embrace the simple routine. I went out and bought a stainless-steel lunchbox, too, because Rocket and I, we eat out of metal bowls, and we look forward to it!"

More Insight from the Recruiting Team

- As with the Emotional Safe Place, use sight, sound, touch, taste and smell to increase the strength of the neural net you're creating.

- As with the Emotional Safe Place, make sure you protect this part of your inner world with some kind of secret passageway.

- MSG members don't have to be alive, and it's fine if they're imaginary.

- MSG members don't have to be human. Frequently, animals join the team. No robots or computers so far, but why not?

- Your support group can be large or small. The cast of characters can come and go. Up to you.

- They may convene in your Emotional Safe Place, but they don't have to.

- There's no one correct way to get their support. You don't have to organize your thoughts into coherent questions. Screaming, venting and sulking are also permitted. Or you can recite poetry or sing.

- Above all things, your MSG members want the best for you.

- They know what's best for you. Maybe it would be good for you to realize your dormant potential or achieve great success in the eyes of the world. But it might also be good for you to take a nap once in a while. Ideally, there are members of your support group who can support very different goals and ideas of wellness.

Whatever other purposes they serve, your MSG and ESP are also mental gymnastics that strengthen your relationship to yourself. Some of us are drawn to the imagery of a neural network; of a brain being strengthened and made resilient by imaginative workouts. I know I do. So: I zoom in on specific areas of my ESP in minute detail, such as the amber color of the drop of sap on my hundred-foot-tall pine tree, the sun shining through it. Or the feeling of the mist from my hundred-foot waterfall on my skin. And I know that I'm also weakening the power of the Emotional

Distress Syndrome to derail my life. Having taught these techniques as long as I have, I can promise that they bring relief, followed by real hope for what lies ahead.

In short, the ESP and MSG really seem to work for me and many of my clients.

The question is "Why?"

What's really going on here? Are we really receiving "messages from the beyond"? Falling into an imaginative trance? Practicing white magic? Are the skeptics out there starting to squirm? Well, take a breath. It's going to be okay. There's nothing mysterious about the power of the ESP and MSG. Let me explain.

SURVIVAL VS. "THRIVAL"

Think about what happens when you confront emotional stress. Though the stressors may come at you from inside or outside yourself, your survival instinct has no "off" switch. But when you activate the part of your brain that cultivates rhyme and reason, you override the survival instinct. Continually furnishing and burnishing an ESP and MSG allows you to gently but firmly remove yourself from adrenaline-fueled anxiety and conjecture. This is always good. Even if you're panicking for good reason—even if there's no good solution to a very pressing problem—wouldn't you rather think it out using the "thrival" part of your brain? Spending time with your ESP and MSG allows you to opt out of survival mode. Now your perspective can be supportive, comforting and friendly.

The more you use the thrival part of your brain, the stronger it gets. Your ESP and MSG are, by definition, unconditional. Whatever you want or need is created in the blink of an eye—an eye that belongs to you and is deployed by you, for the benefit of you. You're giving yourself whatever you need in the moment, without judgment. It may not work this way in the big bad real world, but that's why you create *your* support group and *your* safe place. It's like taking a nutritional supplement of self-esteem.

It's important to understand that the wisdom you hear from the mentors in your MSG must also be in you. The beauty and harmony of your ESP is in part the beauty and harmony in you. So all that rhyme and reason, the architectural touches, the comfortable hammock swinging in the breeze of the perfect climate—it all comes from within. Most of us populate our MSGs with mentors and friends who seem to have what we seem to lack, but even then, it's important to realize that we're actually helping ourselves.

In short, every moment you spend entertaining or helping yourself in your ESP, with your MSG, reinforces the message that you're not broken, even when your survival instinct is screaming the opposite! Every time you go back to your ESP and MSG, you get a clearer picture of wholeness. A former TLEC client had this to say:

> "I had ADHD and addiction issues, and the chronic emotional stress aggravated my addiction and affected my recovery. In my late teens and early twenties, I would act out with extreme emotions—hysterical crying, temper tantrums and violence (screaming, throwing and breaking things). Later, as I began to internalize the stress more, I suffered debilitating anxiety. A specific example of this was taking the MCAT in college. I had ordered an expensive set of study guides months before the test but never opened the books or studied before. The day of the test, I got lost, couldn't find the building, had a meltdown in the

parking lot and barely made it to the test. Was in such a state that I just started filling in the test form bubbles.

It wasn't until I got help with the addiction and the ADHD that I experienced freedom and felt like my life was manageable. Following treatment, I've been in high-stress situations and gone from panic attacks to feeling "frozen" to feeling the stress but not being completely devastated by it.

The ESP and MSG are extremely helpful to me. The ESP made meditation "do-able" for me—I would actually feel renewed, calm, at peace. This was a huge improvement. It's a little difficult to put into words, but having an ESP has given me an enlightened world that I can tap into anytime I wish. It helps calm me when I get frantic and helps give me a different perspective, as well as gratitude. Using my MSG has been especially helpful with building self-confidence, courage and self-nurturing. During therapy sessions I've used my MSG to go back and rescue my past self. It's been instrumental in healing from past shame, hateful thoughts about myself and being able to forgive myself. Using the MSG, my higher power and my current self to nurture and give strength to my old self (with past trauma) has released many of my old emotional land mines. As a result, my reaction to stressors is better, my anxiety is lower (and dissipates faster), and for the first time in my life, I am content with and love myself. This is HUGE."

AND NOW?

You've constructed your Emotional Safe Place and Mental Support Group. Both are an eye's blink away, especially during tough moments. It would be tempting to tell you to go forth and practice these skills until they become a therapeutic routine.

But as I've said before, I believe we're uniquely challenged when it comes to things like routine and structure, even though we may need them as much as—or maybe more than—the next guy. They simply must be customized, by us, for us.

So, really, the only way for you to turn your ESP and MSG into a "therapeutic routine" would be for you to look forward to the process. Which means it has to be fun, challenging, or otherwise engaging—a passion, really. There has to be more to rebuilding yourself than filling in blanks on a chart. I like to think of it as advanced life empowerment. At my workplace, we practice it a lot.

PART THREE:

ADVANCED LIFE EMPOWERMENT

D o you have a moment?
Great, because I'd love to show you around my office, also known as The Life Empowerment Center, TLEC for short.

We're located in South Austin, Texas, home of the best food trucks and live-music venues in the world, in my not-so-humble opinion. I live and work in a vibrant, messy democracy, where PhDs rub shoulders with homeless people (who may have a few PhDs of their own) and more "creatives" from New York and California arrive each day. Summers have hundred-degree highs, winters have blue northers, and the outdoor patios and porches are standing-room-only every month of the year. You've probably seen a "Keep Austin Weird" T-shirt, but I prefer the popular regional bumper sticker that reads, "We're all here because we're not all there." Austin has been a good fit for me, and for a lot of others who weren't sure what they wanted to be when they grew up. You don't necessarily have to grow all the way up in this town. You get extra chances to reinvent yourself—or even to invent yourself for the first time.

It's well known that people with ADHD are easily bored and distracted, and I'm no exception. But I'm lucky to live and work in a town that offers an ever-changing menu of stimulating input. Thank you, Austin!

To get to the TLEC office, you go down a flight of stairs leading from a parking lot through a kind of tropical forest. I've been here 16 years and counting, but it still feels like a slightly enchanted path leading to a slightly enchanted place. I mean, it's my office, but that doesn't mean I can predict what will happen there on any given day. TLEC has never bored me—not once. Something is always developing.

Today, for instance. About halfway through my day, I've seen four clients so far, all with some form of ADHD, all seeking help in managing the beast of the diagnosis. I've been around this particular block a few times, but I never get tired of this particular story. If you met me at a party and we circled around to the topic, you'd get an earful; because there's always something new or newfangled to learn about this condition, and like others with ADHD, I always have a few new obsessions occupying valuable brain space.

My current promising cure (for myself only!) is Bulletproof Coffee. I think I'm ready for my second cup of the morning, which means a trip to the office kitchenette and, with any luck, a chance to run into a few of my office-mates. One door down, there's my wife, Edie, a recently retired art teacher who has reinvented herself as an ADHD strategist and life coach. In the office across the hall from hers, Guy, a former TLEC intern, now an ADHD coach who also teaches the art of meditation.

As I walk down the hall, I hear the gentle but firm sound of Kim, my executive assistant of 16 years, on the phone with a client, and I remember that I'd be lost without her. She serves as a sort of TLEC Mom figure, dispensing unconditional, unshockable organization, acceptance and interest, not just to the people who office here, but to the clients. I also rely on bookkeeping and accounting services to serve as a buffer between me and taxes, licensing and all the other necessary details I'd have a tough time managing on my own.

All of these people—coaches, consultants, executive assistants—form exactly the kind of therapeutic resource community I imagined years ago. Clients now have a bunch of options to choose from. We're a team.

Two members of this team—Kim and Robin, the writing coach who's been camped out on the sofa in the reception area—have just demanded funding for a taco run. I guess you could call it team building?

This afternoon, I look forward to a Life Empowerment group session—all female, all well over fifty, one of whom has spent the past month on a serious thrift-shopping tear and has taken to bringing second-hand gifts for the other women in the group. We'll gather in the group room, with its two comfortable couches, a pristine whiteboard ready for brainstorming, the obligatory Kleenex box and big windows looking out onto the greenbelt. With this group, I suspect, chocolate will be mentioned, or consumed, or both.

Breakfast tacos are more the flavor of the all-male group that officially disbanded a year ago but whose members still support each other through the storms of ADHD. They hold "official" reunions on the first Friday of each month at a local taco joint. Another session that, as an honorary member, I really look forward to.

The rest of my time is taken up with private clients, as it always has been. Every time a new one arrives, I hear a familiar story with a new twist; I feel the empathy that is somehow unique to this new person. Although I don't yet know anything about him or her, and wouldn't presume to guess, we already have something in common.

It usually goes something like this:

They're still not reaching their potential, or they don't seem to be making rational sense to anyone around them, or they've been using either willpower or the sheer force of adrenaline to get things done, but now they're losing balance and they know it. Their career or their marriage or their health is failing. Or—not to be dramatic—all three.

If there's no presenting disaster, they really, really need someone to talk to.

"Who am I supposed to talk to about my ADHD—a normal person? This is a world where the so-called "worried well" are told to suck it up! If I'm not supposed to discuss this constant sense of unease and regret—and I mean, really, it's like an itch!— can I ever disclose the most shameful secrets of all, the fact that I'm bored??? Boredom is painful for a person like me! But I'm not stupid! I know better than to vent about it to my husband. He might take it personally. I guess no one wants to be a casualty of someone else's quest for novelty. But still—I'm so tired of trying to count my blessings, have an attitude of gratitude, get my mind right. In fact, spare me the UNHELPFUL clichés."

This week, I did an intake with a 29-year-old business wunderkind, just diagnosed with ADHD, worried about having destroyed a six-year relationship with a woman he truly loves. And how is it possible that, even after having attending one of the top entrepreneurial MBA programs in the country, he can't seem to find his passion?

I saw an engineer in her mid-forties who sat on her diagnosed-but-untreated ADHD for five years and now must live with the loss of her first marriage, due to an impulsive affair. She struggles with distraction on the job, with feeling that she couldn't possibly be worth her very reasonable salary.

Tomorrow I'll see a software executive who has eighteen years of psychoanalysis under his belt but never addressed the very real problem of growing up with an alcoholic parent. Now he wants to eradicate that what-the-hell-is-wrong-with-me feeling once and for all. Being diagnosed with ADHD has been explosively enlightening for him.

But I'll also see clients I've known for years, who are much further along in the process of life empowerment. Typically, they no longer come in for weekly sessions, just for the occasional tune-up, sometimes with a spouse or child. Or maybe, having completed a few years in one of the TLEC Life Empowerment Groups, they'll come back for a combination reunion and check-in with old friends.

Together, we're seeing that ADHD looks different at the different stages of life. It's sometimes hard to remember the days when the condition was thought to be specific to young children, because I've since diagnosed adults as old as 87. Sometimes it's the milestone of retirement that creates the disruption that drives someone into my office. One woman came to me at 69, in a frazzle of disorganization after having retired from the bowling alley she'd run for years. Without that structure, routine and consistency, not to mention the fun and stimulation of a constant parade of humanity, she went stir-crazy—and only then did the ADHD that had always been her genetic heritage show up and start causing her trouble.

Another older client—78 when he first walked into my office!—had been incredibly accomplished in his career as an attorney. He came to me only after his second wife of 34 years said, "I've had it with you. You need help." In the ensuing year, he made great progress with EMDR and a TLEC Life Empowerment group, came out the other side and created a treatment module for grief counseling and began seeing clients. Talk about living powerfully!

> "I always thought it was important to get in and out of therapy as quick as possible. I wanted the therapist to give me an estimate of the damages and then fix me, like a good mechanic. So I will never forget the light bulb that went on after I'd been going to the Life Empowerment group for a few weeks. Hey, I thought—taking care of my mental health is going to be like going to the gym. I've been working out, one way or another, for most of my adult life. It would never occur to me to think I am "fixed" and quit going! So why would I think that about managing my ADHD? I think my brain needs to work out with these other smart old ladies on a regular basis! Why would I think it's weak to need some EMDR once in a while?"

What that client realized is that dealing with ADHD is an ongoing process, and that asking for help, or continuing your education, won't jeopardize your growing self-reliance. Choosing to thrive is a conscious decision, one we have to make over and over again. There's no shame in requesting a little backup therapy and/or support during the course of your empowered life. Needing a tune-up once in a while doesn't mean you haven't made progress. Knowing when to ask for help—especially before the situation gets out of hand—is a sign of self-sufficiency and recovery.

Can a person actually be said to be "recovered" from ADHD? Possibly, but "recovery" can be a problematic word; there's an element of pass or fail about it. I prefer to think that if we stay focused on navigating our lives, we eventually cross a threshold, after which we're more functional than dysfunctional. I believe we can learn to live powerfully, even to die power-fully. I've had a few clients who contracted terminal illnesses, but because they really understood their ADHD, the way they died was conscious and clear and powerful. They were able to say goodbye, to be emotionally connected and present all the way to the end.

My practice is also full of examples of people who thought they no longer needed certain structures, or certain medications, or who began spending impulsively. Rebuilding your sense of self doesn't mean life's challenges will disappear. You can still get cancer, discover your spouse is having an affair, or learn that something unethical is going on in your business. Things happen. Things change. But for the most part, these people have been able to feel the distress, acknowledge their mistakes, change their actions, check back in, and go on with their lives.

I have my own mood swings and low points. Occasionally I'll still wake up thinking, "This is it, James. You'll never get another new client. The phone has stopped ringing." But since I know that's just brain chemistry talking, I go in to work anyway, and when I look around my work-place, I feel energized and alive. All things considered, there's something authentic going on here. It's worth showing up for. I'm never sorry I came.

What follows is a sort of field guide to advanced life empowerment. It's a collection of principles, theories, tips and tricks that have gotten us through the storms and helped us appreciate the high points. You'll have better results with advanced life empowerment if you've constructed an Emotional Safe Place and Mental Support Group—if you've started building the strong, resilient foundation you'll be standing on for the rest of your life.

Beyond that, remember that you have ADHD, and that any good ADHD solution is personalized. So, to borrow a phrase from the 12-step community, as you read on, *take what you like and leave the rest.*

Co-Existing with Stress

I hate to break this to you, but things are never going to calm down once and for all. This can be hard to hear, especially when you've worked so hard to clean up the damage caused by the emotional distress of ADHD. Surely that should mean you've earned the right to some peace of mind? Well, sure. Once in a while. But there will always be storms and cycles, periods of stress that come and go.

Breaking free of ADHD-induced paralysis often generates a burst of energy, and with energy come positive projects that come with their own sets of stress. Is there such a thing as positive stress? In fact, there is: eustress, the buzz associated with such things as riding a roller coaster at an amusement park, scoring a winning lottery ticket or seeing your dreams come true through hard work and planning. (Or seeing your daydreams come true through no work at all.)

Eustress is the opposite of the popular image of "bad" stress, the blood-pressure escalator, the temper-igniter, the marriage-destroyer—but remember, routine, monotonous tasks can cause us negative stress too. And while there are plenty of ways to disarm "bad" stress in the short run—meditation, exercise, laughter and prayer come to mind—there's no point in trying to make all stress disappear. For instance, right now I have a waiting list of new clients, a book to finish writing, live talks to download on my website; all good problems to have. But how many people can I actually see in one week, and where are my car keys? The existential anxiety doesn't go away. It's not that it's bad; it's just stressful. So live it, embrace it, carry it, carry on.

Seeing your stressors for what they really are, without minimizing or maximizing their seriousness, is the beginning of balance.

Images of Balance

When our resilience isn't well developed yet, managing stress can feel like walking a tightrope. Any misstep leads your brain to perceive a threat, leading to the familiar cascade of ADHD symptoms, leading to the feeling that you're falling, followed by the reality that, yes, you're falling off that rope, hoping there's a net under there somewhere. So you tense up and try like hell not to fall. The constant vigilance, the keeping an eye on yourself, is exhausting.

But as you learn to calm yourself, to keep yourself in balance, the rope gets a little easier to manage, or maybe your coordination improves. Now it's more like a balance beam. As your skills continue to develop, it becomes more of a sidewalk. Eventually, you realize you're walking down a four-lane highway—a scenario that has thrills and risks of its own, but at least you don't have to worry about free-falling into thin air.

Pods of Support

It doesn't get much simpler than this: If you have ADHD, you should try to arrange some kind of buddy system, ideally more than one.

At the most elementary level, we tend to get stuck on those tediously linear tasks—things like tax preparation, filing papers and cleaning out garages. Just having another human body in the room makes a big difference, and if that human body is attached to another ADHD brain, you don't have to explain or justify the urge to procrastinate. Much has been written about the way ADHD adults can help each other through the organizational quandaries of daily life. All of it is true. Seek out, and offer, that kind of help.

If you have addiction issues in your past (or present), you're probably familiar with 12-step recovery groups. I wouldn't have recovered from my own addictions without this kind of help, and I continue to be amazed and impressed at how easy it is to find 12-step groups online and all over the world. They offer the kind of structure that's so important for the ADHD brain, along with the lifeline so necessary to addicts and their loved ones.

Even if you consider yourself a loner, you might benefit from an occasional get-together with others who share your unique brain chemistry. As one of my clients put it, it's "incredibly cool to talk all night without having to run everything through the translator in my head." Check Facebook, Meetup and other social media outlets for an ADHD support group in your area. These groups don't have to be organized around psychotherapy or facilitated by a therapist to do you some real good.

If you're seeing a therapist, though, he or she might be able to recommend a group. It couldn't hurt to ask.

Finally, some of our TLEC clients have spun off and formed their own small pods of support, each organized according to the needs of its participants. There's a business mentoring group, a group of young moms and a group of older women who meet in person only once per month but connect by text almost daily.

In other words, if you can't find a grown-up ADHD group to join, start one. It doesn't have to be complicated or overly organized.

"There is nothing like being in a room with a group of people whose minds all work similarly, whose thoughts jump in the same ways, whose creativity and spontaneity energize, inspire and enlighten me. How can you feel down on yourself when you are surrounded by such amazing, inspiring people and you realize that your brain works just like theirs? A huge confidence boost. It helps me see the amazing benefits of ADHD, not just the frustrations."

Ride the Cycle/Retreat to the Cave

If you have ADHD, the cycle of disruption never entirely disappears. Just because you get your life crystalized and organized doesn't mean the cycle has permanently ended. That's not how a cycle works. Instead, it spins through its highs and lows and eventually comes back to a place of equilibrium.

Remember this when you find yourself on the edge of freaking out, yet you can't really isolate a triggering problem or event. Maybe it's just everyday anxiety, your brain's limbic system perceiving a threat, the way you know it sometimes does. If that's what it is, you know plenty of ways to calm it down.

It might also be helpful to view your moods as a kind of endless wave pattern, without assuming that up is good and down is bad. Take the state of mind known as melancholy. Once I got over being afraid of it, I found not only that I didn't mind it, but that I actually sort of welcomed the downtime. For me, it's a kind of calming, reflective, low-energy state. As long as I don't tense up and try to push melancholy away, it doesn't stay around very long.

Storms happen. Usually you can find a safe place to ride them out. Occasionally you can't: you can see the clouds on the horizon and feel the stress building in your psyche, and maybe you sense that you're going to be fairly worthless in the real world, if only for a few hours. At times like these, I will sometimes allow myself to retreat to my spiritual caves, whether that means ignoring the dark stuff in favor of mindful meditation, or going to my Emotional Safe Place.

Being by yourself and licking your wounds is not the same thing as checking out of reality.

Brutal (Beautiful) Honesty

Sometimes, especially when we're young and don't really understand our inherited genetic condition, it's easiest to just ignore our ADHD. Later on, it's easiest to hope it goes away. Eventually, neither strategy works. So how about this instead: *Stop* ignoring or avoiding your ADHD. Stand in front of it. Look at it. Think of ways you could explain it, to yourself and others.

- Look, this is my genetic code, this is how it affects my thoughts and actions, and this is how it's showing up in me at this particular age.

Think about how your ADHD might impact your future plans. Know your own risk factors.

- I know I have a history with gambling, so I wonder how watching this high-stakes poker tournament might affect me?

- When I get bored, I tend to do impulsive things to make the situation more interesting. Could I do that right now without destroying anything in the process?

- Every time I buy a paper calendar, I lose it. Should I really buy another one, or should I learn to keep my schedule in the cloud?

Since this is who you are and it's not going away, allow yourself to be yourself. Own it. If you say something impulsive, apologize and move on. Maybe, like so many of us, you have a tendency to be disorganized. You might want to remind yourself that in spite of your best efforts, you are going to lose something or forget something. And when that happens, don't say, "I'm such a jerk." Say, "Oh, there's my genetic code," and figure out your next move.

Honestly confronting your ADHD—and the tendencies of others with ADHD—inoculates you against becoming your own character assassin. Speaking of which...

Beware of Hired Killers

In a twisted way, character self-assassination comes naturally to people with ADHD. Berating ourselves, questioning our very right to exist in civil society and talking to ourselves in a sneering, sarcastic way can feel oddly natural and right. Make no mistake, though: It's not.

When your ADHD behaviors are at their most egregious—when you lock yourself out of the car, again, or find yourself in the middle of a screaming fight *picked by you*—it can set off a survival-instinct reaction that's very hard on the body. Adrenaline floods your nervous system. And here's a dirty little secret: A lot of us rely on adrenaline for motivation. Sometimes, not having any better ideas, we do a little self-trash-talking to get the adrenaline to kick in. It can feel almost motivational to scold yourself, in a scornful, disapproving voice. Perhaps your childhood gave you a hair-trigger sensitivity to the subtleties of those voices.

I think of those voices as hired killers, and it's true that they can masquerade as motivational speakers, but I shouldn't have to tell you that this motivation is short-lived. The older we get, the more often we find ourselves kicked to the couch by the negative voices in our heads. Just to be clear, this is not a character-building experience. It doesn't toughen us up. Most of the time, in fact, hired killers have nothing new or enlightening to say. They play an old, worn-out soundtrack: Negativity's Greatest Hits.

Instead of listening to those old tracks for the umpteenth time, you might want to consciously tone down the vitriol. Use all the tools at your command to leech out some of that poison. Now try talking to yourself in a voice that is neither positive nor negative, but curious and observant:

Hired killers are telling me I screwed up again, and they want to know how that could have possibly happened. Okay. What else is new? How bad was this so-called screw-up, on a scale of 1 to 10? Do I need to make amends to someone? How many productive hours are left in this day? What's for lunch?

And later, after the storm has passed:

What did this last storm teach me?

Or try this: Consciously reject the voice of the Hired Killer. When you talk to yourself, be honest, curious and compassionate. It may not come as naturally, at least not at first, but stay with it. Support yourself with self-talk instead of tearing yourself down.

For example: Perhaps you've had the experience of asking people for help without remembering they don't understand the condition you have. They might have good information, but it might not work for someone with ADHD. You might think, *I'm asking for help and it's not working. There's something wrong with me. There always has been.* But instead of piling onto yourself and your (perceived) character defects, ask yourself open-ended questions.

I wonder why his advice didn't work for me?

How likely is it that I could remember those 10 Easy Steps?

And use your compassionate, curious voice to cultivate your self-esteem and self-identity.

Well, I can't use those ideas, but I'm not out of ideas yet. One thing I have a lot of is ideas.

Accept that you'll constantly have to bring your brain back into balance. Don't take it on as something that's wrong with you or bad or broken—and try not to encourage any hired killers who insist the opposite. ADHD isn't your identity. It's something you manage, support and balance. *ADHD can be managed. I would add that it can not only be managed, but also leveraged.* So, more than an obstacle to be overcome, ADHD can be an advantage if you see it for what it is.

Get Un-Stuck

Sometimes, for whatever reason, emotions aren't worth dissecting with a fine-tooth comb. Sometimes it makes more sense to let them go, allowing yourself to come back into balance without a lot of self-management. We all seem to need a place to park distress, to lock it up and walk away for a few hours.

So if you're a natural verbal venter, write. Don't give a second thought to things like grammar and penmanship. Let it flow.

If you're more visual, get your hands on some art supplies and paper, the larger the better. Break out a whiteboard or a blackboard. One of my clients swears by blue painter's tape—you can use it to attach almost anything to a wall. It's nobody's business what you draw or scribble. Leave it up as long as you want or erase it, but don't forget to take a photograph before you do.

Personally, I love mind maps. You can Google mind map or MindMup for more specific guidance, but essentially it's a simple technique. You start with a piece of paper, draw a circle in the center and write a few words describing a stuck emotion, thorny problem or unanswered question.

Then you start drawing spokes attached to bubbles, each representing an aspect of the problem. This can be systematic and ordered or off-the-wall free association:

Just going through this process seems to balance the brain, but you could take it further—you could go back and assign a stress rating to each bubble of text. You could color code it according to a system invented by you. You could stand back and see if a visual pattern emerges, and then see if that pattern gives you some kind of insight.

What's the Next Step?

Sometimes that's the only question you need to ask yourself.

That means you can forget about the Big Picture, the future, the dire implications, the regrets, the looming deadline. Really. This is your (temporary) pass.

What's the next step?

Do that.

Rhyme and Reason:
Intellectual and Emotional Curiosity

Curiosity comes easily for people with ADHD. That's good. Really.

People with ADHD have this perception that curiosity breeds distraction, and that therefore they need to keep it in check. Not necessarily. I think it's possible to channel curiosity, to use it to calm emotional distress.

But then, I'm a therapist, and a therapist is curious by definition. I get to know clients through their life history, through eliciting whatever helps us to untangle the mystery of self-worth. One of the underpinnings of my practice is this: Your entire life history is your most valuable resource. It's a valuable repository of experience, strength, knowledge and wisdom.

And yet most clients come here having looked at their lives as nothing more than a collection of failures. They give me chapter and verse about the shame they feel because they lost focus, again, or got fired, again, or forgot their wife's birthday, again. The emotional stress fills the room. They're "managing" their lives through intensity, chaos and distress. I probably don't have to tell you how hard this is on the body. I do want to tell you that there are better ways to cope.

Imagine you're in the middle of an emotional storm. Instead of going into full anxiety-and-stress mode, imagine hitting the "pause" button— using the tool of mindfulness—and searching for insight. It may seem counterintuitive to drop the judgments and reactions and just look at yourself with compassionate curiosity. It may feel a little weird. Try it anyway, because searching for the rhyme and reason in an uncomfortable moment tends to interrupt the 24/7 stress-programming schedule. It gives your brain a break—just enough to power up the search engine in your brain. Now you can begin to type open-ended questions into the super-computer of your mind and see what kind of answers you get.

Not everyone wants that kind of understanding. Plenty of clients have asked to skip this part. "I don't want to understand this wasteland that is my mind," they say. "I don't want to visit it. I don't even want to live there! So don't tell me to explore this desert—tell me how to FIX it!"

One of the most important skills I've developed is to sit calmly and *not* fix it. Instead, I help clients discover who they are. It's a process of calming down the emotional reactions long enough that they can investigate that "wasteland" and discover lessons of real value.

They need to hear that their ability to reflect on their lives isn't broken. Yes, it may be horribly skewed by an overly active limbic system that sees threat and failure everywhere. But they can learn to calm their brain chemistry—enough to see their lives through a different lens, one that reveals the adventure hidden beneath the chronic stress. It really is possible, in other words, to look at your life from a place of observation and curiosity and to be fascinated. To discover, in fact, that the storehouse of a life's experience is not an inconsequential place.

If you're brave enough to go inside your head and look around, you'll find:

- Everything you already know about how to solve challenges and repair mistakes.

- All your life experience, including the great adventures.

- All your visions and dreams; all the ways you want to move forward.

You don't have to be highly intellectual or analytical to mine this information. Just ask yourself—calmly and compassionately—what do I know about this? What information is already there? Is my mind really a desert, or is that a palm tree I see over there?

What do you discover when you quietly pay attention, replacing judgment with curiosity?

ADHD gives us a hair-trigger sensitivity to being thrown out of balance. Looking for rhyme and reason puts us into neutral, witnessing mode, which helps calm the rumination and brain chatter. Better, it can help you see the inquiry as a kind of treasure hunt. Rather than being repetitive or predictable, your emotional stress will yield something intriguing or interesting—certainly not boring. What you learn about yourself may not make sense to anyone else, but that's okay.

You can start engaging with rhyme and reason at any age, but when you start young, it gets really interesting. I have a handful of clients who first started coming to me as school-age children, whose parents brought them in, and who may have finished therapy years ago but still come in from time to time for an emotional checkup or just to say hi. Can you imagine? A foundation of real, internal strength, as opposed to feeling broken, wrong, stupid or different?

This is what I see in ADHD children who've grown up in households full of love, tolerance, patience and support. This is not to say that these clients don't have challenges or sometimes feel like human balls of stress, but they seem to recover and rebound without too much trouble, and their lives continue to be kick-ass adventures!

These kids grew up in safe environments, by which I don't mean boring or unchallenging, but kind of excitingly safe—the kind of atmosphere that inspires a child to discover who she really is. In this atmosphere, a child can clearly understand how he's different from others. He can accept the fact that his brain works differently from that of most people he'll encounter. But rather than leading straight to emotional distress, that knowledge comes with the freedom to explore, with ideas that aren't limited or shut down with brainstorming and silliness. These kids make it to adulthood without losing the feeling that their emotional voices are valuable, without worrying about looking, or being, stupid. And I have to think that all that resilience comes from a spirit of curious exploration. It makes sense to them…and to most children, actually.

Compassionate curiosity will help you see your life as more than a series of mistakes and forgotten appointments. You may begin to see that some of your emotional reactions are the result of everyday stress, stress that can be managed quickly and easily, as opposed to some deep and permanent moral failing on your part.

The fascinating thing is that no matter how well you understand the theory, when you're in the middle of a cycle, you'll feel blindsided. Stay in front of the anxiety anyway, secure in the knowledge that it's going to release. Nobody ever stayed anxious forever. It's building up, and there will be a release, and you will come back into balance. All you're trying to find is a bit of philosophy to keep you connected to yourself. It doesn't have to make sense to anyone but you.

Mayday! Mayday!
Staying the Course During a Storm

At the risk of repeating myself, there *will* be storms. The tools and techniques we use at TLEC should reduce the number and duration you experience, but they're going to happen. Furthermore, although most storms are manageable squalls, every once in a while you're going to experience a hurricane—an emotional bad patch that may last longer than a few days. Your version of a Category 5 storm may look a lot like clinical depression or what used to be called a nervous breakdown. Your loved ones may grow concerned or annoyed. The important thing is to think about how to manage it in advance, and, if at all possible, to get some kind of emergency-preparedness plan in place.

But you can also read this section if you're in the middle of a big storm, or feel one coming on:

"I will now state the obvious. I don't regulate emotions very well. I think I have a storm coming on."

"I'm hypersensitive. It feels like a big bruise. Such jealousy when I start noticing other people's accomplishments! I have a hard time feeling happy for someone who's accomplished anything! I wish people would quit publishing novels. I wish their kids would quit getting into college. I'm even jealous of someone who can fill the car with gas. This can't be good."

You're the Navigator, Even Now

As I've said, and as you know by now, it can be very difficult to "activate the insight-oriented part of your brain" during a genuine emotional storm. This is when the temptation kicks in—to surrender to nasty self-talk, to throw down one of your classic temper tantrums, to sink into a depression. During a storm, it's hard even to remember that you're in charge of this expedition known as your life, much less think insightful thoughts about where you're headed.

It might be helpful to return to the theme of navigation.

In the following scene, written by Herman Melville, the great recorder of nautical disasters, an 1840s-era ship is trying to round Cape Horn in the midst of a horrific storm:

"Here the scene was awful. The vessel seemed to be sailing on her side, plunging through the sea, which undulated over her sides in milk-white billows of foam, drenching the men on the fore-yard. The deck was alive with the whole strength of the ship's company, the sea cast a glare on their uplifted faces in the panic-stricken crowd. It now blew a hurricane. The spray flew over the ship in floods. The gigantic masts seemed about to snap under the world-wide strain of the three entire topsails."

The ship's captain orders the crew to turn the ship *away* from the wind, to "fly away from the gale." The crew refuses to follow his orders, choosing instead to obey Mad Jack, an experienced, if unranked, sailor who tells them to turn the ship directly *into the wind*. His order is nearly impossible to carry out, but it saves the ship and all of their lives. And, Melville says, the decision to steer "hard up, into the teeth of the gale, although attended with more appalling appearances, is in reality the safer of the two."

Whenever the concept of rhyme and reason sounds a little too neat and pretty to be useful, I think of that scene. Because there's a place for rhyme and reason on the high seas during hurricanes. Sometimes, all you can do is summon your courage, turn INTO the wind, and hang on to the wheel. Your brain is not broken. You can still think. You can still make good, if tough, decisions. You still have courage. The storm will end.

Remember

Your limbic system is reacting to a threat. This threat may or may not exist. Your brain is more than a limbic system. See: meditation, mindfulness, spirituality, intuition and humor.

Remember

Your Emotional Safe Place and Mental Support Group are an eye's blink away.

Remember

Sometimes a storm is a metamorphosis. If you keep your eyes open and stay conscious of what's going on around you, if you just keep walking in the face of anxiety, you will eventually experience a kind of release. I don't know how long it will take, but eventually you'll arrive at a new place—new insight, new decision, new peace—having realized there was no other way to arrive at this destination.

Remember to take care of yourself.

Self-Care 101

- See your practitioner, psychotherapist, MD, massage therapist, workout buddy, whomever. Find the number. Make the call.
- Find that pod of support. Reach out to ADHD buddies, any and all. Find the number, make the call.
- Simplify everything. Cut down on commitments. Try to do some percentage of what you usually do, but don't be too hard on yourself. If you usually go for a run, could you try a short walk? If you can't walk, spend a little time outside. If you can't make yourself shower, wash your face.
- If you take prescription medication, keep taking it.
- Process, process, process, in whatever way works for you. Talk aloud to yourself, write in your journal, get it out on paper some other way, yell, sing, swear. No one needs to hear you doing this. If you have something to say to someone, you can get to it later, when you feel a little stronger and more focused.

Give yourself permission to go back to bed for the day.

Not the week.

Eat some chocolate.

Not ALL the chocolate.

Find a way to laugh.

Self-Talk

Imagine someone from your Mental Support Group is observing you during this storm—or go to your Emotional Safe Place to hear from this person. What does this observer say about the emotions you're feeling so strongly? Is there any wisdom available for you? Any action you should take?

Ask for and access compassion, from any part of yourself. This doesn't always come naturally. So:

Tell yourself something simple and positive, such as *I'm okay. I'm still in the game.*

Remind yourself of the things that still give you pleasure, even if pleasure seems like an academic concept at the moment. If you need to, make a list.

Be forgiving of yourself, as you would a good friend. Give yourself praise—not for doing anything in particular, but for being who you are.

Be ready for the hired killers to show up, because they will. Let them know their services won't be required just now. Visualize a metal box for their venom, a box that can be locked up and buried deep underground.

If you feel you "must" think apocalyptic thoughts, try assigning a short, specific time of day devoted to just that. Try worrying, hard, and in great detail, from 4 to 4:15 pm.

Accept that you may not be capable of everything you expect yourself to do during the course of your regular life—not now, and maybe not in the future. It might be more helpful, though, to conserve emotional energy by thinking of what you actually *can* expect from yourself, today. If other people appear to be more competent and capable than you do, so what? Things are seldom as they seem. Right now it's more important for you to accept who you are and what you can and cannot do.

"What I hate is the voice that says ugh, here I am again, in the storm! I tried so hard to avoid ever having this happen ever again, and here it is, and this time, it will never go away! But you know what my husband used to say? 'Getting upset because here you are, in the storm again, and using that as an excuse to dump all over yourself, is as pointless as getting upset over being constipated. Because A, you know what to do about it, and B, you know it will pass.'"

HOW TO MAKE THE STORM LAST LONGER

- Go tense. Hyperventilate. Suck it up. Don't cry!
- Swear that this will never happen again.
- Refuse all reasonable offers of help.
- Make this your mantra: NOBODY UNDERSTANDS ME.
- Pick a fight with a loved one, or lure your spouse into a session of talking things over that goes on past midnight, with nothing resolved.
- Decide that you don't have ADHD. Try to blend in.
- Pull yourself up. Try harder.

Remember

Every storm ends. Even this one.

Emergency Communications Protocol

Even if you feel hopelessly stuck in your own head, try, for a moment, to be grateful for the normal people in your life who know how weird you are and stick around anyway. Who continue to do things that suddenly seem too hard—whether it's earning a living, raising the children, folding the laundry, or keeping the house from burning down and the world from blowing up. Even when you feel godawful, you can build a reservoir of goodwill, one drop at a time, by saying "Please," "Thank you" and "How was your day?"

Plan a few other things to say, as well. I know that may not be your strong suit, but this is important, because someone you care about is likely to ask if something is wrong. As much as you may want to grunt monosyllabically or burst into tears and vent non-stop, try to explain the circumstances of your storm in a way that is short, sweet and considerate. Yes, you're lonely, and yes, you're in turmoil, but if you love this person, don't beg them, with words or actions, to fix you. Fixing you shouldn't be their responsibility. Fixing you shouldn't be a thing!

Consider making the following points, or some variation thereof, instead:

- Looks like I'm in a state of overwhelm.

- It's not your fault. You didn't do anything to cause this.

- Sometimes it takes a while, but I promise you, it will pass.

If you blurt out something you regret, you can always say, "I'm sorry, that didn't come out quite right." Or "This isn't a good time to talk. Can I take 15 minutes to decompress?" Or just "Sorry."

If your loved one offers you advice, listen to it, and thank them for it, and do what you can to soothe yourself. But remember that non-ADHD solutions won't always make sense, and that translation can get pretty frustrating for everyone. If you start coming unwound, take a break and do what you need to do to soothe yourself.

Or read ADHD as a Second Language, below.

ADHD as a Second Language

Knowing how to interact with others in a meaningful way is not an easy task when you have ADHD. It's oddly comforting to realize that as much as ninety percent of the time, other people just won't get you. There will be gaffes, gaffes and more gaffes. You will discover your own foot in your own mouth. You will wonder who let the bull into the china shop, and then discover that you are the bull, as well as the landlord of the china shop. The point is, you'll be disruptive once in a while. In the middle of a conversation, you'll be distracted by the shiny object du jour. Your body may be actively engaged in romance, but your brain may morph into an Elvis impersonator and leave the building.

My advice is to feel the awkwardness for a moment, then move on. That's easier said than done, because ADHD people have a tendency to shut down in social situations. But I believe in embracing our awkwardness instead. Is there any other choice?

Feel what you feel, apologize if it's appropriate to do so, try to see the humor in the situation, and keep going. Concentrate on bridging the gap—doing what you can to connect to others. This requires letting go of our sometimes intense self-focus. That's okay. Your navel's not going anywhere. You can gaze at it later.

Despite your best efforts, you'll occasionally say something completely inappropriate. You'll hear it come out of your mouth, by which time it will be too late to take it back. A short, pre-worded apology is nice to have in reserve.

I can't think about marriage—or communication, love, partnership or wisdom—without thinking of my longtime clients Keith and Andrea. A married couple, both with ADHD, they were my clients together and separately for more than a decade. As their therapist, I was privileged to witness their deep, messy, passionate, always evolving relationship, and even though Keith died several years ago, I'm still learning from the books he wrote and from Andrea, who remains a presence at TLEC. Much of what they had to say to each other was deep and personal, but Andrea has given me permission to share one small item.

Like all other ADHD-ers, Keith and Andrea each occasionally suffered from foot-in-mouth disease. It made for some interesting, if short-lived, arguments, a lot of which started with *"What* did you just say to me?" After a while, they developed a stock response. Whoever had just made the ridiculous, inappropriate ADHD-inspired comment would say, "Oops. Can I have a do-over?"

Oops: Can I Have a Do-Over?
Happily Married With ADHD

Edie, my wife of 26 years, doesn't have ADHD. But as you can imagine, she knows a lot about it. She tells me that one of the most important things she's learned is *what to let go of and when to get out of the way.* As long as my ADHD-related behavior isn't affecting her or the family, she'll allow me to work things out on my own, and she's cultivated the stamina to stay in front of the stress and be confident of getting through it. She tells me that it takes emotional strength, tolerance, compassion and true under-standing of the ADHD brain.

How does the non-ADHD spouse cultivate that kind of self-knowl-edge and growth? For now, let me just say this: It's critically important that a spouse take care of herself, take time for herself, and learn not to personalize what the ADHD has disrupted.

I will now acknowledge that ADHD puts enormous stress on a marriage.

ADHD adults are extremely shiny objects early on in a relationship. They're spontaneous and exciting. They're fun to be around, and they attract people who want to be around someone who's fun to be around! At this stage, it can be hard to understand that a life partner is actually someone you select *for life*. Because ADHD adults aren't *always* fun to be around. Life is a lot longer than that.

The constancy of the problem that doesn't go away can wear on a relationship. It takes serious determination and compassion to ride the wave of problems based on disorganization, time management, clutter, strategies working for a while then not working, forgetfulness, and on and on. Understand that the ADHD will be a constant stressor.

If this sounds messy, passionate living always is. And so are all healthy marriages. Whatever doesn't kill you, as a couple, makes you stronger. Really. Not kidding. Obviously, good conflict-resolution skills are a must.

A few words for the spouse of the human diagnosed with ADHD: Patience. Tolerance. Forgiveness. Patience. And again, patience.

And now a few words for the other half of the couple—the human being with ADHD:

You are going to be disruptive, and it's going to feel, at times, as if your spouse doesn't understand you very well at all. Cultivate patience!

Let's say you're exhibiting a repeating pattern of ADHD behavior, and you know it drives your spouse crazy, and yet you can't seem to stop. From the outside, that can look a lot like willfulness—as if you're being a jerk on purpose. Most of the time, you're not—in my experience, the heart of the ADHD adult is kind and loving as opposed to manipulative and button-pushing. But your behaviors can be crazy-making. What to do?

Surrender is the only option. When you've upset the equilibrium in your home—forgetting important dates, diving into a shiny-yet-ill-advised hobby—acknowledge it, apologize for it, and then sit back and take in your partner's response. This is the hard part, make no mistake. Your job is to reflect back in a way that lets them know you were listening attentively.

Then, explain how you'll mitigate the disruption.

It's very difficult to listen actively to your partner's distress *and* decide how to repair the damage *and* manage your own distress. It's a monumental task, this surrendering to responsibility, but it's the most effective thing you can do.

Here's what you *can't* do: fix your partner's anger or frustration, rescue him or her from grief or loneliness, roll the clock back twenty years, or turn yourself into a different person altogether.

But you're not helpless, either.

When things begin to escalate with your spouse, neutralize and objectify the situation by talking about it from a position of detached interest, as if you're seeing it on a table.

I understand you're upset. I hear you. And this seems to be getting out of hand.

Keep talking about it and describing it. Sometimes that will slow down the intensity of the emotions. If not, get some distance; take a break.

This isn't a good time. I'm going to take a walk. I'll be back.

When you're out walking, you can work on calming yourself and your emotional distress. You know what ADHD is and isn't. You know how it can be a threat to your relationship. But you don't need to let yourself feel battered.

Look, I know I have problems with this. I'll do the best I can with what I have. I'm gonna keep moving forward, and let's both do that.

Moving on is a good idea and a healthy impulse. But don't move on before—or instead of—delivering a sincere apology. If you're the non-ADHD spouse, it can be quite dispiriting to be on the receiving end of a rushed and not-very-soul-searching "I'm sorry! Okay???" If you're the spouse with ADHD, the prospect of apologizing may fill with you with anxiety. What if no one believes you? What if your partner accepts your apology and then piles on an extra helping of criticism? What if your heartfelt mea culpa comes off as cavalier?

Well, you really have no choice here but to

1. slow down
2. listen, and
3. tell the truth.

I choose to believe that, outside of outright abuse, my marriage is always going to be there. To put it another way, I choose *not to have a choice* about divorce or leaving. Too many people see divorce as a convenient option. Interestingly, I have no idea if Edie ever made that choice, but that's okay, because we do have one value in common: A commitment to working on our own stuff in our own way. If you don't do that, you can end up leading parallel lives, a dynamic where you live separately, in the same house, with occasional intersections involving kids and friends. It's not a messy way to live, but it's not intimate, either, and what is a marriage without messy intimacy?

"The Emotional Distress Syndrome has been present in my life with my husband for a long time. His ability to manage his lack of focus, organizational skills, ability to plan and/or prioritize have not become better or worse over time. It is what it is! Hard! What *has* changed is my husband's ability to recognize these limitations and deal with them in a more productive way. At the beginning of our marriage, he dealt with the stress by yelling, with rude or mean comments, anger, stomping around the house (among other things). Now, after many years of therapy, he recognizes trigger points and has developed tools to more calmly deal with his stressful feelings. If the house is full of children and he has lost track of time hyper-focusing on something, instead of exploding at either me or our daughter, he'll say, "I'm in a bubble. I have to leave to stay focused."

"Learning to understand and manage the Emotional Distress Syndrome has been life-changing for my family. Before, I didn't use to think my (ADHD) husband cared about anything, because he processed so quickly and moved sporadically from one thing to the next with very little emotion. He would come home in the evening and ask about my day, but as soon as I started talking, he would answer a text message with one hand and stick the other into a basketball game with the kids. We argued over daily details but didn't understand how to address the larger issue of distress. After talking with James, I began to see that my husband did care—about the kids, me, work, community, and that he could never tell any of us no. Instead of taking offense all the time, I learned to recognize how hard he was trying, and to help him find ways to succeed. I learned to say things like, "It's okay if you can't talk about my day right now. Make your phone call, finish the basketball game, eat something! We'll talk at 9 p.m."

Parenting Our Greatest Teachers

Children can be your greatest reward and your greatest challenge, in ways you could never imagine and never thought to prepare for. Sometimes you can see yourself inside your children. Other times, you get to see them demonstrating skills and passions far beyond your own. And sometimes it all meshes, in a beautiful way that really does stop time. This is true, I think, whether there's ADHD in the family or not.

That said, ADHD can certainly stress a family system, and we who have this condition have a serious responsibility not to let it overwhelm our parenting. Kids know disruption when they see it, even if they don't say anything at the time. So, while we may not be able to erase every trace of our disorganization and distraction, we can make a conscious decision not to catch our kids up in our personal tornadoes. More important, we can commit to reflecting on our own behavior and how it affects our families.

If you never appear to question your own actions or thought processes, your children will see your behavior as unreasonable or even dictatorial. If you do engage in honest self-reflection, your kids will see you as a genuine, honest person, which is really all you can be. I like to think that my kids see my foibles, but they also see me managing myself. I don't have a problem asking them for advice and support, and I hope they'll ask me for some in return.

Your children really do have the potential to be your greatest teachers. Not that they're responsible for taking care of you, but they hold up a little mirror that reflects your genetics and the effects of your behavior. You may not always want to see that little mirror, but screw up your courage and look. You will not turn to stone!

Both my sons have given me incredible insights into my own life. I'll never forget a moment when Gabe, my older son, was five. I must have gotten a little too hyper and playful, as I admit I sometimes do. He looked at me and said, "Dad, I need you to be an adult right now." I stood there with my mouth open. Then I thanked him. Then I honored his request and turned back into a grownup.

If you've been trying to set yourself up as a supreme parental authority figure, forget it. There may be some family systems where that works, but an ADHD adult is not likely to be able to pull it off. In my opinion, the core of parenting is knowing that children are their own individual selves, from the very beginning. You need to respect them by giving them their own sense of age-appropriate independence and by not expecting them to be someone they're not. They are not, for instance, you.

It's critically important to follow your child's passions as they develop. You want them to grow up to be curious, observant, exploring kids who naturally find their own interests—which won't necessarily be your interests. Here's an example: Having grown up in a large, competitive family, I would sometimes feel gleefully happy when I beat my (very young) sons at easy board games. Luckily, I snapped out of that as soon as I noticed I was doing it, but the subject of sports was loaded. During my own high school years, I'd quit the varsity baseball team out of anger at the coach and regretted that decision all my life. So when my son Jules decided against playing organized sports, I felt a level of disappointment. Maybe I thought he could have the experience I'd impulsively denied myself. Maybe I thought he showed real potential. Either way, I had to be careful not to disrupt him that way, because my feelings and desires were mine, not his. In any case, both my sons eventually chose to be physically active adults, which makes me very happy.

Here's the short version of my advice for parents with ADHD:

- Be real.

- Pay attention. I know we have trouble with attention, but these are your children. This is important.

Here's the slightly longer version: Work on yourself seventy percent of the time. Be an example of an adult who acknowledges his mistakes, makes amends when necessary and lives life on life's terms. Work on supporting your kids thirty percent of the time. Provide them with opportunities and structure and raw materials. Then stay out of their way and watch the magic of their lives unfold.

A Final Little Storm, with a Shiny Ending

In the final weeks of finishing this book, I was thrown off course by a cluster of perplexing emotions. On one hand, I was excited—I had been writing and re-writing since 1989, through good times and bad, since before my sons were born. At times, I worried the manuscript would never actually become a book. And now, here I was, awash in having-your-dreams-come-true accelerated heartbeat sensations. Followed, about a second later, by the be-careful-what-you-wish-for syndrome. No sooner had I heaved that final sigh of writer's relief than I began spiraling up, up, up in a marketing frenzy! Wasn't it time to blog, tweet, package, platform, TED-talk and hobnob?

While throwing out these many and brilliant ideas at meetings with Robin, my writing coach, I literally could not sit still. But she could. She sat there on the sofa and looked at me, with the exact "weary eye" I described in "ADHD as a Second Language."

Sure enough, even though I had completed the daunting task of preparing my book for publication, I was still an adult with ADHD, and something about the prospect of going public with my work had set off a little storm—a squall. Once I was able to settle down, I could see that my whole process was a perfect illustration of almost every principle in this book.

So, if you're in the mood for one last story, here it is: the tale of how my grand ambition got reduced to a ball of melted sand filled with hot air.

First, I finished the book. I felt good. Job well done, deadline met.

Second, I felt vaguely unsettled. I did *not* pause to examine these feelings, probably because they made me uncomfortable. They may have been something along the lines of *Who's actually going to buy this book? Does anyone read anymore? I'm a provider! If I don't handle every one of these details myself, my family will starve, and plus, everyone will know I was a fraud and an imposter. Do I really know what I'm doing? The TLEC appointments line will never ring again. Kim will clean out her desk. There I'll be, eating the lone taco of despair, in an empty office.* It was that, or thoughts to that effect.

Third, I pushed those thoughts away by brainstorming umpteen marketing platforms, lunching with a half-dozen potential publicists, commissioning a revenue spreadsheet and telephoning ADHD experts about the prospect of keynoting an as-yet-un-scheduled conference.

Fourth, I did not answer this question, asked by Robin: "What is it that you actually *want* to do with your time, other than what you already do? Does sitting at a Barnes and Noble behind a pile of books sound fun to you? Would you like to be an event planner?"

Fifth, I got the message from my publisher that the book would now be going into copy-editing and production mode. It was not time to market or launch. While meditating, I got the message from Ecclesiastes that to everything, there is a time and purpose. From my Mental Support Group, I got the message that now was the time for me to *sit on my hands.* (It's what my mother-in-law used to tell Edie when she got too busy.) When I engaged my engine of curiosity and observation, without judgment, I could see that it was time to let the experts do their job.

Sixth, okay, but I was antsy. And I actually had some free time for a change.

Seventh, I remembered that I very much wanted to learn to blow glass. Of course I did—what could be shinier or more magical? What "practical" use could there possibly be for this artisanal skill, and who gets to give me permission to learn it? Me, that's who. I found a studio in town and signed up for a class. It starts in two weeks.

Eighth, I called David, my best friend of 35 years, and ran my idea past him. (We all need pods of support.) His advice? "When blowing glass, never inhale!"

Ninth, and finally, the little storm subsided. Any rhyme and reason will become apparent later, perhaps long after I've taken the class. Maybe it won't have anything to do with the round balls of iridescence filled with hot air, but my intuition tells me otherwise.

About James Ochoa

James Ochoa is a licensed professional counselor and the founder and director of The Life Empowerment Center (TLEC) in Austin, Texas. Born and raised in Houston, in a large, loving family, he was inspired by the challenges of his own learning differences to study psychology, receiving his B.A. from the University of Texas at Austin and his M.Ed. in Counseling & Guidance from Texas State University in San Marcos, Texas.

His clinical experience includes residential and outpatient treatment centers, psychiatric hospitals, prisons and his own private practice, with clients ranging in age from 4 to 84. The Life Empowerment Center offers a wide range of treatments, all in support of his passion for helping adults with ADHD to live powerfully in the midst of their emotional storms. In addition, he offers insight- and action-based coaching and counseling to clients from all walks of life, including the business world.

His certification in the Results Coaching Systems, a neuroscience-based executive coaching model, has been a key factor in guiding clients toward creative problem-solving in their personal and professional lives. In 1994, James was certified in EMDR, a clinical treatment model that uses the science of the mind to help clients confront and resolve emotional distress. Since 1993, he has offered educational groups for adults with ADHD as well as longer-term goal-focused Life Empowerment groups. In 2016, he began offering continuing-education workshops and consultations for other clinicians seeking a better understanding of the Emotional Distress Syndrome, along with strategies for helping their clients to overcome it and live full lives.

James lives and works with his wife, Edie Vitemb, an ADHD strategist, life coach and artist, in Austin, Texas. They have two sons, Gabe and Jules, and one very handsome brindled cattle dog.

For more information about James and his services go to www.jamesochoa.com.

Index

Lightning Source UK Ltd.
Milton Keynes UK
UKHW021842231218
334483UK00014B/328/P

9 780996 983907

"Focused Forward *gets it!* If you or someone you care about has the adult version of ADHD, read this book. Written by a man who's worked in the trenches his whole career, this book is full of practical tips as well as a deep understanding for what this widely misunderstood condition is truly like. A hugely valuable contribution to the treatment of adult ADHD."

–Edward M. Hallowell, M.D.,
New York Times–bestselling author of *Driven to Distraction*

"Mr. Ochoa's ground-breaking concept of the Emotional Distress Syndrome of adult ADHD now gives us a previously missing but critical understanding, as well as innovative tools to soothe the ADHD soul. This book offers a rare combination of warmth and wisdom—I'm already recommending it to my clients."

–Sari Solden, MS, LMFT, bestselling author of
Women with Attention Deficit Disorder and *Journeys Through ADDulthood*

FINALLY—MAKE PEACE WITH YOUR ADHD BRAIN

If you have ADHD, every day can be a battle. You fight to stay in control. To meet your obligations. To *not screw up.* But what you might not know about—what's even more damaging—is the constant, corrosive emotional stress of a lifetime of wondering *what the hell is wrong with you.*

In *Focused Forward: Navigating the Storms of Adult ADHD*, author James M. Ochoa, LPC tackles the fallout from ADHD—a PTSD-like condition he calls the Emotional Distress Syndrome. With the practical, proven guidance of someone who's been there, he helps readers:

- Understand the link between ADHD and emotional distress
- Master eight essential coping tools
- Construct an Emotional Safe Place
- Recruit a Mental Support Group
- And more

With wisdom, humor and plenty of empathy, *Focused Forward* will help you move past the pain and shame toward a future of possibility, balance and joy.

James Ochoa is a therapist, writer and speaker who investigates the conundrums, challenges and rewards of adult ADHD—all of which he's experienced first-hand, being a diagnosed "ADHD-er" himself. Equally grounded in neuroscience and intuition, his personal brand of therapy is uniquely empathetic, often transformative. Visit www.jamesochoa.com

Price: $18.95   Printed in U.S.A.

ISBN 978-0-9969839-0-7
90000

9 780996 983907